Science 6
Teacher's Guide

CONTENTS

Author: **Alpha Omega Publications**

Editor: Alan Christopherson, M.S.

Alpha Omega Publications®

804 N. 2nd Ave. E., Rock Rapids, IA 51246-1759
© MMI by Alpha Omega Publications, Inc. All rights reserved.
LIFEPAC is a registered trademark of Alpha Omega Publications, Inc.

OVERVIEW

SCIENCE

Curriculum Overview
Grades 1–12

	Grade 1	Grade 2	Grade 3
LIFEPAC 1	YOU LEARN WITH YOUR EYES • Name and group some colors • Name and group some shapes • Name and group some sizes • Help from what you see	THE LIVING AND NONLIVING • What God created • Rock and seed experiment • God-made objects • Man-made objects	YOU GROW AND CHANGE • Air we breathe • Food for the body • Exercise and rest • You are different
LIFEPAC 2	YOU LEARN WITH YOUR EARS • Sounds of nature and people • How sound moves • Sound with your voice • You make music	PLANTS • How are plants alike • Habitats of plants • Growth of plants • What plants need	PLANTS • Plant parts • Plant growth • Seeds and bulbs • Stems and roots
LIFEPAC 3	MORE ABOUT YOUR SENSES • Sense of smell • Sense of taste • Sense of touch • Learning with my senses	ANIMALS • How are animals alike • How are animals different • What animals need • Noah and the ark	ANIMAL GROWTH AND CHANGE • The environment changes • Animals are different • How animals grow • How animals change
LIFEPAC 4	ANIMALS • What animals eat • Animals for food • Animals for work • Pets to care for	YOU • How are people alike • How are you different • Your family • Your health	YOU ARE WHAT YOU EAT • Food helps your body • Junk foods • Food groups • Good health habits
LIFEPAC 5	PLANTS • Big and small plants • Special plants • Plants for food • House plants	PET AND PLANT CARE • Learning about pets • Caring for pets • Learning about plants • Caring for plants	PROPERTIES OF MATTER • Robert Boyle • States of matter • Physical changes • Chemical changes
LIFEPAC 6	GROWING UP HEALTHY • How plants and animals grow • How your body grows • Eating and sleeping • Exercising	YOUR FIVE SENSES • Your eye • You can smell and hear • Your taste • You can feel	SOUNDS AND YOU • Making sounds • Different sounds • How sounds move • How sounds are heard
LIFEPAC 7	GOD'S BEAUTIFUL WORLD • Types of land • Water places • The weather • Seasons	PHYSICAL PROPERTIES • Colors • Shapes • Sizes • How things feel	TIMES AND SEASONS • The earth rotates • The earth revolves • Time changes • Seasons change
LIFEPAC 8	ALL ABOUT ENERGY • God gives energy • We use energy • Ways to make energy • Ways to save energy	OUR NEIGHBORHOOD • Things not living • Things living • Harm to our world • Caring for our world	ROCKS AND THEIR CHANGES • Forming rocks • Changing rocks • Rocks for buildings • Rock collecting
LIFEPAC 9	MACHINES AROUND YOU • Simple levers • Simple wheels • Inclined planes • Using machines	CHANGES IN OUR WORLD • Seasons • Change in plants • God's love never changes • God's Word never changes	HEAT ENERGY • Sources of heat • Heat energy • Moving heat • Benefits and problems of heat
LIFEPAC 10	WONDERFUL WORLD OF SCIENCE • Using your senses • Using your mind • You love yourself • You love the world	LOOKING AT OUR WORLD • Living things • Nonliving things • Caring for our world • Caring for ourselves	PHYSICAL CHANGES • Change in man • Change in plants • Matter and time • Sound and energy

Grade 4	Grade 5	Grade 6	
PLANTS • Plants and living things • Using plants • Parts of plants • The function of plants	CELLS • Cell composition • Plant and animal cells • Life of cells • Growth of cells	PLANT SYSTEMS • Parts of a plant • Systems of photosynthesis • Transport systems • Regulatory systems	LIFEPAC 1
ANIMALS • Animal structures • Animal behavior • Animal instincts • Man protects animals	PLANTS: LIFE CYCLES • Seed producing plants • Spore producing plants • One-celled plants • Classifying plants	BODY SYSTEMS • Digestive system • Excretory system • Skeletal system • Health and diseases	LIFEPAC 2
MAN'S ENVIRONMENT • Resources • Balance in nature • Communities • Conservation and preservation	ANIMALS: LIFE CYCLES • Invertebrates • Vertebrates • Classifying animals • Relating function and structure	PLANT AND ANIMAL BEHAVIOR • Animal behavior • Plant behavior • Plant-animal interaction • Cycles and balance in nature	LIFEPAC 3
MACHINES • Work and energy • Simple machines • Simple machines together • Complex machines	BALANCE IN NATURE • Needs of life • Dependence on others • Prairie life • Stewardship of nature	MOLECULAR GENETICS • Reproduction • Inheritance • DNA and mutations • Mendel's work	LIFEPAC 4
ELECTRICITY AND MAGNETISM • Electric current • Electric circuits • Magnetic materials • Electricity and magnets	TRANSFORMATION OF ENERGY • Work and energy • Heat energy • Chemical energy • Energy sources	CHEMICAL STRUCTURE • Nature of matter • Periodic Table • Diagrams of atoms • Chemical changes	LIFEPAC 5
PROPERTIES OF MATTER • Properties of water • Properties of matter • Molecules and atoms • Elements	RECORDS IN ROCK: THE FLOOD • The Biblical account • Before the flood • The flood • After the flood	LIGHT AND SOUND • Sound waves • Light waves • The visible spectrum • Colors	LIFEPAC 6
WEATHER • Causes of weather • Forces of weather • Observing weather • Weather instruments	RECORDS IN ROCK: FOSSILS • Fossil types • Fossil location • Identifying fossils • Reading fossils	MOTION AND ITS MEASUREMENT • Definition of work • Rate or force of doing work • Laws of motion and gravitation • Change in motion	LIFEPAC 7
THE SOLAR SYSTEM • Our solar system • The big universe • Sun and planets • Stars and space	RECORDS IN ROCK: GEOLOGY • Features of the earth • Rock of the earth • Forces of the earth • Changes in the earth	SPACESHIP EARTH • Shape of the earth • Rotation and revolution • Eclipses • The solar system	LIFEPAC 8
THE PLANET EARTH • The atmosphere • The hydrosphere • The lithosphere • Rotation and revolution	CYCLES IN NATURE • Properties of matter • Changes in matter • Natural cycles • God's order	ASTRONOMY AND THE STARS • History of astronomy • Investigating stars • Major stars • Constellations	LIFEPAC 9
GOD'S CREATION • Earth and solar system • Matter and weather • Using nature • Conservation	LOOK AHEAD • Plant and animal life • Balance in nature • Biblical records • Records of rock	THE EARTH AND THE UNIVERSE • Plant systems • Animal systems • Physics and chemistry • The earth and stars	LIFEPAC 10

Science 600 Curriculum Overview

	Grade 7	Grade 8	Grade 9
LIFEPAC 1	**WHAT IS SCIENCE** • Tools of a scientist • Methods of a scientist • Work of a scientist • Careers in science	**SCIENCE AND SOCIETY** • Definition of science • History of science • Science today • Science tomorrow	**OUR ATOMIC WORLD** • Structure of matter • Radioactivity • Atomic nuclei • Nuclear energy
LIFEPAC 2	**PERCEIVING THINGS** • History of the metric system • Metric units • Advantages of the metric system • Graphing data	**STRUCTURE OF MATTER I** • Properties of matter • Chemical properties of matter • Atoms and molecules • Elements, compounds, & mixtures	**VOLUME, MASS, AND DENSITY** • Measure of matter • Volume • Mass • Density
LIFEPAC 3	**EARTH IN SPACE I** • Ancient stargazing • Geocentric Theory • Copernicus • Tools of astronomy	**STRUCTURE OF MATTER II** • Changes in matter • Acids • Bases • Salts	**PHYSICAL GEOLOGY** • Earth structures • Weathering and erosion • Sedimentation • Earth movements
LIFEPAC 4	**EARTH IN SPACE II** • Solar energy • Planets of the sun • The moon • Eclipses	**HEALTH AND NUTRITION** • Foods and digestion • Diet • Nutritional diseases • Hygiene	**HISTORICAL GEOLOGY** • Sedimentary rock • Fossils • Crustal changes • Measuring time
LIFEPAC 5	**THE ATMOSPHERE** • Layers of the atmosphere • Solar effects • Natural cycles • Protecting the atmosphere	**ENERGY I** • Kinetic and potential energy • Other forms of energy • Energy conversions • Entropy	**BODY HEALTH I** • Microorganisms • Bacterial infections • Viral infections • Other infections
LIFEPAC 6	**WEATHER** • Elements of weather • Air masses and clouds • Fronts and storms • Weather forecasting	**ENERGY II** • Magnetism • Current and static electricity • Using electricity • Energy sources	**BODY HEALTH II** • Body defense mechanisms • Treating disease • Preventing disease • Community health
LIFEPAC 7	**CLIMATE** • Climate and weather • Worldwide climate • Regional climate • Local climate	**MACHINES I** • Measuring distance • Force • Laws of Newton • Work	**ASTRONOMY** • Extent of the universe • Constellations • Telescopes • Space explorations
LIFEPAC 8	**HUMAN ANATOMY I** • Cell structure and function • Skeletal and muscle systems • Skin • Nervous system	**MACHINES II** • Friction • Levers • Wheels and axles • Inclined planes	**OCEANOGRAPHY** • History of oceanography • Research techniques • Geology of the ocean • Properties of the ocean
LIFEPAC 9	**HUMAN ANATOMY II** • Respiratory system • Circulatory system • Digestive system • Endocrine system	**BALANCE IN NATURE** • Photosynthesis • Food • Natural cycles • Balance in nature	**SCIENCE AND TOMORROW** • The land • Waste and ecology • Industry and energy • New frontiers
LIFEPAC 10	**CAREERS IN SCIENCE** • Scientists at work • Astronomy • Meteorology • Medicine	**SCIENCE AND TECHNOLOGY** • Basic science • Physical science • Life science • Vocations in science	**SCIENTIFIC APPLICATIONS** • Measurement • Practical health • Geology and astronomy • Solving problems

Grade 10	Grade 11	Grade 12	
TAXONOMY • History of taxonomy • Binomial nomenclature • Classification • Taxonomy	**INTRODUCTION TO CHEMISTRY** • Metric units and instrumentation • Observation and hypothesizing • Scientific notation • Careers in chemistry	**KINEMATICS** • Scalars and vectors • Length measurement • Acceleration • Fields and models	LIFEPAC 1
BASIS OF LIFE • Elements and molecules • Properties of compounds • Chemical reactions • Organic compounds	**BASIC CHEMICAL UNITS** • Alchemy • Elements • Compounds • Mixtures	**DYNAMICS** • Newton's Laws of Motion • Gravity • Circular motion • Kepler's Laws of Motion	LIFEPAC 2
MICROBIOLOGY • The microscope • Protozoan • Algae • Microorganisms	**GASES AND MOLES** • Kinetic theory • Gas laws • Combined gas law • Moles	**WORK AND ENERGY** • Mechanical energy • Conservation of energy • Power and efficiency • Heat energy	LIFEPAC 3
CELLS • Cell theories • Examination of the cell • Cell design • Cells in organisms	**ATOMIC MODELS** • Historical models • Modern atomic structure • Periodic Law • Nuclear reactions	**WAVES** • Energy transfers • Reflection and refraction of waves • Diffraction and interference • Sound waves	LIFEPAC 4
PLANTS: GREEN FACTORIES • The plant cell • Anatomy of the plant • Growth and function of plants • Plants and people	**CHEMICAL FORMULAS** • Ionic charges • Electronegativity • Chemical bonds • Molecular shape	**LIGHT** • Speed of light • Mirrors • Lenses • Models of light	LIFEPAC 5
HUMAN ANATOMY AND PHYSIOLOGY • Digestive and excretory system • Respiratory and circulatory system • Skeletal and muscular system • Body control systems	**CHEMICAL REACTIONS** • Detecting reactions • Energy changes • Reaction rates • Equilibriums	**STATIC ELECTRICITY** • Nature of charges • Transfer of charges • Electric fields • Electric potential	LIFEPAC 6
INHERITANCE • Gregor Mendel's experiments • Chromosomes and heredity • Molecular genetics • Human genetics	**EQUILIBRIUM SYSTEMS** • Solutions • Solubility equilibriums • Acid-base equilibriums • Redox equilibriums	**CURRENT ELECTRICITY** • Electromotive force • Electron flow • Resistance • Circuits	LIFEPAC 7
CELL DIVISION & REPRODUCTION • Mitosis and meiosis • Asexual reproduction • Sexual reproduction • Plant reproduction	**HYDROCARBONS** • Organic compounds • Carbon atoms • Carbon bonds • Saturated and unsaturated	**MAGNETISM** • Fields • Forces • Electromagnetism • Electron beams	LIFEPAC 8
ECOLOGY & ENERGY • Ecosystems • Communities and habitats • Pollution • Energy	**CARBON CHEMISTRY** • Saturated and unsaturated • Reaction types • Oxygen groups • Nitrogen groups	**ATOMIC AND NUCLEAR PHYSICS** • Electromagnetic radiation • Quantum theory • Nuclear theory • Nuclear reaction	LIFEPAC 9
APPLICATIONS OF BIOLOGY • Principles of experimentation • Principles of reproduction • Principles of life • Principles of ecology	**ATOMS TO HYDROCARBONS** • Atoms and molecules • Chemical bonding • Chemical systems • Organic chemistry	**KINEMATICS TO NUCLEAR PHYSICS** • Mechanics • Wave motion • Electricity • Modern physics	LIFEPAC 10

MANAGEMENT

STRUCTURE OF THE LIFEPAC CURRICULUM

The LIFEPAC curriculum is conveniently structured to provide one teacher handbook containing teacher support material with answer keys and ten student worktexts for each subject at grade levels two through twelve. The worktext format of the LIFEPACs allows the student to read the textual information and complete workbook activities all in the same booklet. The easy to follow LIFEPAC numbering system lists the grade as the first number(s) and the last two digits as the number of the series. For example, the Language Arts LIFEPAC at the 6th grade level, 5th book in the series would be LA 605.

Each LIFEPAC is divided into 3 to 5 sections and begins with an introduction or overview of the booklet as well as a series of specific learning objectives to give a purpose to the study of the LIFEPAC. The introduction and objectives are followed by a vocabulary section which may be found at the beginning of each section at the lower levels, at the beginning of the LIFEPAC in the middle grades, or in the glossary at the high school level. Vocabulary words are used to develop word recognition and should not be confused with the spelling words introduced later in the LIFEPAC. The student should learn all vocabulary words before working the LIFEPAC sections to improve comprehension, retention, and reading skills.

Each activity or written assignment has a number for easy identification, such as 1.1. The first number corresponds to the LIFEPAC section and the number to the right of the decimal is the number of the activity.

Teacher checkpoints, which are essential to maintain quality learning, are found at various locations throughout the LIFEPAC. The teacher should check 1) neatness of work and penmanship, 2) quality of understanding (tested with a short oral quiz), 3) thoroughness of answers (complete sentences and paragraphs, correct spelling, etc.), 4) completion of activities (no blank spaces), and 5) accuracy of answers as compared to the answer key (all answers correct).

The self test questions are also number coded for easy reference. For example, 2.015 means that this is the 15th question in the self test of Section II. The first number corresponds to the LIFEPAC section, the zero indicates that it is a self test question, and the number to the right of the zero is the question number.

The LIFEPAC test is packaged at the centerfold of each LIFEPAC. It should be removed and put aside before giving the booklet to the student for study.

Answer and test keys have the same numbering system as the LIFEPACs and appear at the back of this handbook. The student may be given access to the answer keys (not the test keys) under teacher supervision so that he can score his own work.

A thorough study of the Curriculum Overview by the teacher before instruction begins is essential to the success of the student. The teacher should become familiar with expected skill mastery and understand how these grade level skills fit into the overall skill development of the curriculum. The teacher should also preview the objectives that appear at the beginning of each LIFEPAC for additional preparation and planning.

TEST SCORING and GRADING

Answer keys and test keys give examples of correct answers. They convey the idea, but the student may use many ways to express a correct answer. The teacher should check for the essence of the answer, not for the exact wording. Many questions are high level and require thinking and creativity on the part of the student. Each answer should be scored based on whether or not the main idea written by the student matches the model example. "Any Order" or "Either Order" in a key indicates that no particular order is necessary to be correct.

Most self tests and LIFEPAC tests at the lower elementary levels are scored at 1 point per answers; however, the upper levels may have a point system awarding 2 to 5 points for various answers or questions. Further, the total test points will vary; they may not always equal 100 points. They may be 78, 85, 100, 105, etc.

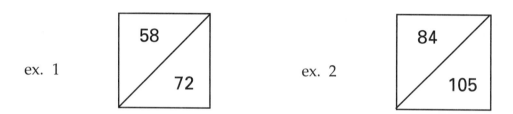

A score box similar to ex.1 above is located at the end of each self test and on the front of the LIFEPAC test. The bottom score, 72, represents the total number of points possible on the test. The upper score, 58, represents the number of points your student will need to receive an 80% or passing grade. If you wish to establish the exact percentage that your student has achieved, find the total points of his correct answers and divide it by the bottom number (in this case 72.) For example, if your student has a point total of 65, divide 65 by 72 for a grade of 90%. Referring to ex. 2, on a test with a total of 105 possible points, the student would have to receive a minimum of 84 correct points for an 80% or passing grade. If your student has received 93 points, simply divide the 93 by 105 for a percentage grade of 89%. Students who receive a score below 80% should review the LIFEPAC and retest using the appropriate Alternate Test found in the Teacher's Guide.

The following is a guideline to assign letter grades for completed LIFEPACs based on a maximum total score of 100 points.

LIFEPAC Test = 60% of the Total Score (or percent grade)
Self Test   = 25% of the Total Score (average percent of self tests)
Reports   = 10% or 10* points per LIFEPAC
Oral Work   = 5% or 5* points per LIFEPAC
*Determined by the teacher's subjective evaluation of the student's daily work.

Example:

LIFEPAC Test Score	=	92%	92	x	.60	=	55 points
Self Test Average	=	90%	90	x	.25	=	23 points
Reports						=	8 points
Oral Work						=	4 points

TOTAL POINTS = 90 points

Grade Scale based on point system:

100	–	94	=	A
93	–	86	=	B
85	–	77	=	C
76	–	70	=	D
Below		70	=	F

TEACHER HINTS and STUDYING TECHNIQUES

LIFEPAC Activities are written to check the level of understanding of the preceding text. The student may look back to the text as necessary to complete these activities; however, a student should never attempt to do the activities without reading (studying) the text first. Self tests and LIFEPAC tests are never open book tests.

Language arts activities (skill integration) often appear within other subject curriculum. The purpose is to give the student an opportunity to test his skill mastery outside of the context in which it was presented.

Writing complete answers (paragraphs) to some questions is an integral part of the LIFEPAC Curriculum in all subjects. This builds communication and organization skills, increases understanding and retention of ideas, and helps enforce good penmanship. Complete sentences should be encouraged for this type of activity. Obviously, single words or phrases do not meet the intent of the activity, since multiple lines are given for the response.

Review is essential to student success. Time invested in review where review is suggested will be time saved in correcting errors later. Self tests, unlike the section activities, are closed book. This procedure helps to identify weaknesses before they become too great to overcome. Certain objectives from self tests are cumulative and test previous sections; therefore, good preparation for a self test must include all material studied up to that testing point.

The following procedure checklist has been found to be successful in developing good study habits in the LIFEPAC curriculum.

1. Read the introduction and Table of Contents.
2. Read the objectives.
3. Recite and study the entire vocabulary (glossary) list.
4. Study each section as follows:
    a. Read the introduction and study the section objectives.
    b. Read all the text for the entire section, but answer none of the activities.
    c. Return to the beginning of the section and memorize each vocabulary word and definition.
    d. Reread the section, complete the activities, check the answers with the answer key, correct all errors, and have the teacher check.
    e. Read the self test but do not answer the questions.
    f. Go to the beginning of the first section and reread the text and answers to the activities up to the self test you have not yet done.
    g. Answer the questions to the self test without looking back.
    h. Have the self test checked by the teacher.
    i. Correct the self test and have the teacher check the corrections.
    j. Repeat steps a–i for each section.

5. Use the SQ3R* method to prepare for the LIFEPAC test.
6. Take the LIFEPAC test as a closed book test.
7. LIFEPAC tests are administered and scored under direct teacher supervision. Students who receive scores below 80% should review the LIFEPAC using the SQ3R* study method and take the Alternate Test located in the Teacher Handbook. The final test grade may be the grade on the Alternate Test or an average of the grades from the original LIFEPAC test and the Alternate Test.

> *SQ3R: Scan the whole LIFEPAC.
> Question yourself on the objectives.
> Read the whole LIFEPAC again.
> Recite through an oral examination.
> Review weak areas.

GOAL SETTING and SCHEDULES

Each school must develop its own schedule because no single set of procedures will fit every situation. The following is an example of a daily schedule that includes the five LIFEPAC subjects as well as time allotted for special activities.

Possible Daily Schedule

8:15	–	8:25	Pledges, prayer, songs, devotions, etc.
8:25	–	9:10	Bible
9:10	–	9:55	Language Arts
9:55	–	10:15	Recess (juice break)
10:15	–	11:00	Mathematics
11:00	–	11:45	Social Studies
11:45	–	12:30	Lunch, recess, quiet time
12:30	–	1:15	Science
1:15	–		Drill, remedial work, enrichment*

*Enrichment: Computer time, physical education, field trips, fun reading, games and puzzles, family business, hobbies, resource persons, guests, crafts, creative work, electives, music appreciation, projects.

Basically, two factors need to be considered when assigning work to a student in the LIFEPAC curriculum.

The first is time. An average of 45 minutes should be devoted to each subject, each day. Remember, this is only an average. Because of extenuating circumstances, a student may spend only 15 minutes on a subject one day and the next day spend 90 minutes on the same subject.

The second factor is the number of pages to be worked on in each subject. A single LIFEPAC is designed to take 3 to 4 weeks to complete. Allowing about 3-4 days for LIFEPAC introduction, review, and tests, the student has approximately 15 days to complete the LIFEPAC pages. Simply take the number of pages in the LIFEPAC, divide it by 15 and you will have the number of pages that must be completed on a daily basis to keep the student on schedule. For example, a LIFEPAC containing 45 pages will require 3 completed pages per day. Again, this is only an average. While working a 45 page LIFEPAC, the student may complete only 1 page the first day if the text has a lot of activities or reports, but go on to complete 5 pages the next day.

Long range planning requires some organization. Because the traditional school year originates in the early fall of one year and continues to late spring of the following year, a calendar should be devised that covers this period of time. Approximate beginning and completion dates can be noted on the calendar as well as special occasions such as holidays, vacations, and birthdays. Since each LIFEPAC takes 3-4 weeks or eighteen days to complete, it should take about 180 school days to finish a set of ten LIFEPACs. Starting at the beginning school date, mark off eighteen school days on the calendar and that will become the targeted completion date for the first LIFEPAC. Continue marking the calendar until you have established dates for the remaining nine LIFEPACs making adjustments for previously noted holidays and vacations. If all five subjects are being used, the ten established target dates should be the same for the LIFEPACs in each subject.

FORMS

The sample weekly lesson plan and student grading sheet forms are included in this section as teacher support materials and may be duplicated at the convenience of the teacher.

The student grading sheet is provided for those who desire to follow the suggested guidelines for assignment of letter grades is found on page 3 of this section. The student's self test scores should be posted as percentage grades. When the LIFEPAC is completed, the teacher should average the self test grades, multiply the average by .25 and post the points in the box marked Self Test Points. The LIFEPAC test percentage grade should be multiplied by .60 and posted. Next, the teacher should award and post points for written reports and oral work. A report may be any type of written work assigned to the student, whether it is a LIFEPAC or additional learning activity. Oral work includes the student's ability to respond orally to questions which may or may not be related to LIFEPAC activities or any type of oral report assigned by the teacher. The points may then be totaled and a final grade entered along with the date that the LIFEPAC was completed.

The Student Record Book which was specifically designed for use with the Alpha Omega curriculum provides space to record weekly progress for one student over a nine week period as well as a place to post self test and LIFEPAC scores. The Student Record Books are available through the current Alpha Omega catalog; however, unlike the enclosed forms, these books are not for duplication and should be purchased in sets of four to cover a full academic year.

WEEKLY LESSON PLANNER

Week of:

Subject	Subject	Subject	Subject
Monday			

Subject	Subject	Subject	Subject
Tuesday			

Subject	Subject	Subject	Subject
Wednesday			

Subject	Subject	Subject	Subject
Thursday			

Subject	Subject	Subject	Subject
Friday			

WEEKLY LESSON PLANNER

			Week of:

	Subject	Subject	Subject	Subject
Monday				

	Subject	Subject	Subject	Subject
Tuesday				

	Subject	Subject	Subject	Subject
Wednesday				

	Subject	Subject	Subject	Subject
Thursday				

	Subject	Subject	Subject	Subject
Friday				

Student Name _____ Year _____

Bible

LP #	Self Test Scores by Sections					Self Test Points	LIFEPAC Test	Oral Points	Report Points	Final Grade	Date
	1	2	3	4	5						
01											
02											
03											
04											
05											
06											
07											
08											
09											
10											

History & Geography

LP #	Self Test Scores by Sections					Self Test Points	LIFEPAC Test	Oral Points	Report Points	Final Grade	Date
	1	2	3	4	5						
01											
02											
03											
04											
05											
06											
07											
08											
09											
10											

Language Arts

LP #	Self Test Scores by Sections					Self Test Points	LIFEPAC Test	Oral Points	Report Points	Final Grade	Date
	1	2	3	4	5						
01											
02											
03											
04											
05											
06											
07											
08											
09											
10											

Student Name _____   Year _____

Mathematics

LP #	Self Test Scores by Sections 1	2	3	4	5	Self Test Points	LIFEPAC Test	Oral Points	Report Points	Final Grade	Date
01											
02											
03											
04											
05											
06											
07											
08											
09											
10											

Science

LP #	Self Test Scores by Sections 1	2	3	4	5	Self Test Points	LIFEPAC Test	Oral Points	Report Points	Final Grade	Date
01											
02											
03											
04											
05											
06											
07											
08											
09											
10											

Spelling/Electives

LP #	Self Test Scores by Sections 1	2	3	4	5	Self Test Points	LIFEPAC Test	Oral Points	Report Points	Final Grade	Date
01											
02											
03											
04											
05											
06											
07											
08											
09											
10											

NOTES

INSTRUCTIONS FOR SCIENCE

The LIFEPAC curriculum for grades two through twelve was written with the daily instructional material written directly in the LIFEPACs. The student is encouraged to read and follow his own instructional material, thus developing independent study habits. The teacher should introduce the LIFEPAC to the student, set a required completion schedule, complete teacher checks, be available for questions regarding both subject content and procedures, administer and grade tests, and develop additional learning activities as desired. Teachers working with several students may schedule their time so that students are assigned a quiet work activity when it is necessary to spend instructional time with one particular student.

The Teacher Notes section of the Teacher's Guide lists the required or suggested materials for the LIFEPACs and provides additional learning activities for the students. The materials section refers only to LIFEPAC materials and does not include materials which may be needed for the additional activities. Additional learning activities provide a change from the daily school routine, encourage the student's interest in learning, and may be used as a reward for good study habits.

If you have limited facilities and are not able to perform all the experiments contained in the LIFEPAC curriculum, the Science Project List for grades 3-12 may be a useful tool for you. This list prioritizes experiments into three categories: those essential to perform, those which should be performed as time and facilities permit, and those not essential for mastery of LIFEPACs. Of course, for complete understanding of concepts and student participation in the curriculum, all experiments should be performed whenever practical. Materials for the experiments are shown in Teacher Notes - Materials Needed.

Science Projects List

Key

(1) = Those essential to perform for basic understanding of scientific principles.

(2) = Those which should be performed as time permits.

(3) = Those not essential for mastery of LIFEPACs.

S = Equipment needed for home school or Christian school lab.

E = Explanation or demonstration by instructor may replace student class lab work.

H = Suitable for homework or for home school students. (No lab equipment needed.)

Science 601

601.A	(2)	S
601.B	(1)	H
601.C	(1)	S
601.D	(1)	H&S
601.E	(1)	H&S
601.F	(1)	S
601.G	(2)	H

Science 602

602.A	(1)	H
602.B	(1)	H
602.C	(1)	H
602.D	(2)	S
602.E	(2)	S

Science 603

603.A	(2)	H
603.B	(2)	H
603.C	(2)	H

Science 604

604.A	(1)	S
604.B	(1)	H
604.C	(1)	S
604.D	(3)	H
604.E	(2)	H

Science 605

605.A	(3)	H
605.B	(1)	H
605.C	(1)	S
605.D	(1)	S

Science 606

606.A	(1)	H&S
606.B	(1)	E
606.C	(1)	H
606.D	(1)	H
606.E	(2)	H
606.F	(1)	H
606.G	(1)	H
606.H	(1)	S
606.I	(1)	H

Science 607

607.A	(1)	S
607.B	(1)	Sor H
607.C	(1)	H
607.D	(1)	H

Science 608

608.A	(2)	H
608.B	(1)	H
608.C	(2)	H

Science 609

Star Colors	(1)	H
609.A	(1)	S
609.B	(1)	S
609.C	(2)	S
609.D	(2)	H
609.E	(3)	H
609.F	(2)	E

Science 610

None

Materials needed for LIFEPAC

Required:

growing plant
4 kernels of corn
4 tall, thin bottles
soda crackers
iodine solution
2 small baby-food jars
Benedict's solution or
    glucose test strips
4 radish or corn seeds
1 plastic bag
paper towels
scissors
stapler
2 thumbtacks
hand lens
water
food coloring (red or blue)

celery stick with leaves
tall baby food jar or glass
metric ruler
fresh leaf of lettuce
single-edged razor blade
microscope
microscope slide and slip cover

Suggested:

plant publications from county agent
Pyrex container (about 250 ml)
alcohol
hot plate
iodine solution
test tube
encyclopedia

Additional Learning Activities

Section I Photosynthesis System

1. Have your students place several plants on the window sill. Turn several of them slightly each day. Let others remain in one position. Compare the plants at the end of two weeks.

2. Place several plants in different types of light, including the darkness of a closet. Compare plants at the end of two weeks.

3. Have the students examine different fall leaves under a microscope. How are they different from the green leaf section?

4. Have the students examine the root of a plant. Then, have them describe the nodules on the plant.

5. Look up several desert plants in an encyclopedia. Compare those plants to plants with leaves.

6. Plant some morning glory plants. Observe the time that the flower blooms. Why does this happen?

Section II Transport System

1. Dissect a plant.

2. Make cuttings of a fast-growing plant such as philodendron or coleus. Have each student grow his cutting in water and then plant it.

3. Go outside with a friend and select several plant stems that look different. Try to locate the pith and vascular bundles.

4. With a classmate or friend, make a large poster showing the parts of a plant. Label the parts.

Section III The Regulatory System

1. Place several plants in your classroom. Let your students take care of them.

2. With several classmates, soak some radish seeds for three hours. Then plant them in cut-off milk cartons. In some of them, add nothing but water. In the others, add house plant fertilizer. Compare the growth of the plants.

3. Repeat the above activity, but plant the seeds in different types of soil (sandy, clay, etc.), adding no fertilizer, only water.

4. Visit a local nursery and ask one of the workers to explain how and why bushes are pruned to make them full. Encourage your students to ask any other questions that might interest them about landscaping, plant care, etc.

5. Investigate how plants are grown organically. Why are organically grown plants better for your body? Write a report (minimum 2 pages) about what you learn.

Materials Needed for LIFEPAC

Required:

  hot plate or stove burner
  Pyrex beaker (about 250 ml)
  Rennet tablet or rennin
  10 ml whole milk
  water
  2 test tubes with stoppers or 2 tall, thin bottles with lids
  10 drops of cooking oil
  honey
  starch
  masking tape
  glucose test strips
  1 drop of iodine solution
  dialysis membrane or semi-permeable membrane (2 squares, 5cm x 5cm)
  2 dental rubber bands
  2 small baby food jars
  2 small bottles that will fit easily inside the baby food jar

Suggested:

  clear limewater (To make limewater, buy lime from a garden supply store and mix 1 tsp. with water in a half full quart jar of water. Stir or shake for 10 min. Let sit for 24 hrs.) Use just the top clear portion of the solution.
  hand air pump
  two soda straws
  2 baby food jars
  rubbing alcohol
  water
  2 cotton balls
  2 baby food jar lids
  watch with second hand

Additional Learning Activities

Section I Digestive System & Section II Excretory System

1. Ask a doctor for a discarded gastro-intestinal X-ray for the students to examine.

2. Invite a dentist to speak to your class.

3. With a friend, build a model of a tooth to show to your class.

4. Research the path of a hamburger through the body.

5. Prepare a two minute speech on the proper way to clean your teeth. Present the speech to your class.

6. Show a video or filmstrip on the circulatory and excretory systems.

7. Take the pulse rate of several of your friends after various activities; for example, walking, reading, jogging, or running hard. What are their breathing rates? Make a chart to show your findings.

8. With a friend, test the effects of rest and activity by placing a test tube over your thumb. One of you should sit and rest and one exercise vigorously for ten minutes. Be careful not to break the test tube. Compare the perspiration in the two test tubes after ten minutes.

9. Trace the path of a drop of blood completely through the circulatory system from the right ventricle to the right auricle.

10. Write a one- to two-page report on the importance of blood types.

Section III Skeletal System

1. Show a filmstrip or video on the skeletal system.

2. As a friend moves his arms and legs, feel the movement in the joints. Identify the type of joint.

3. With a friend, check a first aid book for treatment of fractures and sprains. Practice making a sling for your arm.

4. Investigate a bone disease, such as arthritis. Write a one- to two-page report on the effects and treatment of the disease.

5. Visit a local emergency room or urgent care center. Make a report on what you learn there.

6. With your parents' permission, investigate the possibility of becoming a volunteer at your local hospital.

Materials Needed for LIFEPAC

Required:
    piece of card stock or heavy paper
       (10cm x 10cm)
    scissors

Suggested:
    several goldfish in bowls
    fish food

Additional Learning Activities

Section I Animal Behavior

1. Make a list on the board of different types of animal responses your students can think of.

2. Discuss with your class the many examples of instinctive behavior found in nature.

3. With a friend, make a poster-size diagram of the brain or a neuron. Label the parts. Encourage the students to display their posters in the classroom.

4. With a classmate or friend, visit a local pet store or zoo. Observe the behavior of the various animals. In what ways are the behaviors different?

5. Form a good habit or break a bad habit by following the guidelines given in your LIFEPAC.

6. Observe a pet over a period of days. Make a list of different types of responses you see your pet exhibit.

Section II Plant Behavior

1. Purchase a Venus-flytrap or a mimosa plant for your classroom. Discuss the three types of tropisms with your students. Why is it necessary to know about them if you are going to grow plants?

2. With a classmate or friend, design and set up an experiment to show the effects of one of the tropisms discussed in this LIFEPAC.

3. Plant several large seeds, such as lima bean seeds. After all the plants germinate, dig them up to see if all of them were planted so that the root section grew downward and the stem section upward. What happened to the seeds that were not planted like this?

Section III Plant-Animal Interaction

1. Prepare a bulletin board on the different types of biomes. Have your students bring in pictures of plants and animals for each type.

2. Discuss what happens to a biome when man begins to urbanize it.

3. With a friend, make a poster for your classroom. Show how a food chain works.

4. Select a terrestrial biome. Research your topic on the Internet or in a library and write a two-page report on it.

5. In a two-page report, describe the differences and similarities between the marine and fresh water biomes.

Materials Needed for LIFEPAC

Required:
  seed catalog
  magnifying glass
  black paper
  plastic knife
  toothpick
  fresh flower
  lima beans
  Lifesaver (mint)
  PTC Taste Papers

pea seeds
ruler marked in millimeters
marine and fresh water biomes.

Suggested:
  albino corn seed
  sorghum seeds
  petri dish
  pots of soil

Additional Learning Activities

Section I Reproduction

1. Have the students perform an experiment growing tubes from pollen grains in sugar water. They will need toothpicks, a depression slide, a cover slip, sugar water, and a fresh flower. (Sugar water is made from 1 teaspoon of sugar dissolved in 1 cup of water.) A regular microscope slide edged with a ring of Vaseline will also serve as a depression slide. Use a clean toothpick to scrape off pollen into sugar water. Add a cover slide. DO NOT SMASH COVER SLIDE DOWN!

2. Examine the flower and discuss these questions with your student(s).

    a. How many sepals are there?

    b. How many petals does the flower have?

    c. What color are the petals on your flowers? Sepals?

3. Count the petals and the anthers.

4. Locate the stigma and the style.

5. Determine whether the flower is cross-pollinated. (If stigma is in the flower below anthers and pollen, flower is self-pollinated).

6. Make a poster of a flower and label all of the parts.

7. Research and write a one-page (minimum) paper on mitosis.

Section II Inheritance

1. Show your student(s) how to use a Punnett Square. The Punnett Square is necessary for recording genetic data. It provides basic understanding of the possible combinations of genes. If you were not able to solve the Punnett Square for guinea pigs, follow step-by-step this method. Bb times Bb where black dominates over white.

    Step 1. First draw a square with four blocks.

    Step 2. Place the genes for one parent at the top of the square and the genes for the other parent to the left side.

Step 3. Bring down the genes from the top of the square into the blocks as indicated by the arrows in Step 2. Then bring the genes from the left side and add them to each block just as you did above. Be sure the dominant gene is always listed first. (Example Bb, not bB).

Step 4. What fraction of the guinea pigs have black coats? To determine this, note that every block with dominant B will be black. BB, Bb, and Bb make a total of 3 out of 4 or 3/4. Refer to the chart and see that 3/4 equals 75%. Notice that only 1 block is bb (white). This is 1 out of 4 or 1/4, which equals 25%.

Step 5. What fraction of the guinea pigs are purebred black? Notice that only 1 block is purebred black (BB). This is 1 out of 4, or 1/4.

Step 6. What fraction of the guinea pigs are hybrid black (Bb)? Only 2 blocks are hybrid Bb; 2 out of 4 equals 2/4 or 1/2 hybrid black.

2. With a friend, visit a nursery. Inquire about grafting and budding of various plants.

3. Research the work of Gregor Mendel. Report to the class on any new information you discover.

Section III DNA, Mutations, and the Environment

1. With a friend, make a picture-type report on albinos. Try to collect pictures of albino mice, rabbits, and white and green variegated plants.

2. Prepare a detailed report on the Washington navel orange. Make some drawings for your bulletin board. Explain how seedless plants are grown from year to year since they do not have seeds.

3. Prepare a report on the work of Dr. Herman J. Muller:

   (a) What did he discover concerning X-rays and genetics?

   (b) What little animal did he use for experiments?

4. Give a report on some of the mutations of the fruit fly known as Drosophila. Include one of the drawings of a mutant fly. This could be a mutation from normal red-eyed to white-eyed flies. Or perhaps you could make a drawing of a wingless form. Indicate in your report whether or not these mutations are harmful.

5. Give a report on the effects of mutations:

   (a) Make a list of harmful effects of mutations and

   (b) explain how man uses mutations in plants. Consult a genetics textbook for information on mutations.

Materials needed for LIFEPAC

Required:

copper penny
iodine solution
cotton swab
small pan
hot plate or Bunsen burner
metal and plastic spoons
phenolphthalein solution
vinegar
baking soda
ammonia

Suggested:

balloon
square dish
small block of wood or rock
soda pop
plastic glass or test tube
limewater
soda straw
yellow, pink, and light orange crayons

LIMEWATER INSTRUCTIONS

1. Mix 1 tsp. lime in a half quart of water.
2. Stir at least 10 minutes.
3. Let stand for 24 hours.
4. Pour off clear liquid (limewater) on top.

Additional Learning Activities

Section I Chemical Structure

1. Discuss some of the gases found in the air. Mention that, even though oxygen is absolutely necessary for us to breathe, nitrogen is the major gas in the atmosphere.

2. Discuss the use of inert gases such as argon and neon in man-made lights.

3. Discuss the fact that chemists have placed matter into three distinct classes: solids, liquids, and gases. There are many stages between these three classes. For example, putty or molding clay are not entirely solid. There are no in-between stages for gases. A substance is either gaseous or not. Some substances, such as iodine, go directly from the solid stage to a gas. Liquid iodine is a solid dissolved in alcohol to make a solution. Pure iodine is either a solid or sublimes into a gas when heated. Carbon dioxide can be solid or gas.

4. Have your student(s) make a list of metals (use the symbols chart for the names). Have them use the Internet or go to the library to look up special uses for these metals. Examples: Titanium, a light metal, is used in the manufacture of airplanes. Iron is used in the manufacture of steel. Nickel is used in magnets along with iron. Have pupils consult an outside source for the meaning and examples of alloys.

5. Have your student(s) make a pie-shaped graph (or another type of graph) showing the gases in the air. Consult an encyclopedia or the Internet for the components of air.

6. Have your student(s) research and discuss the oxidation and corrosion of metals. Example: Pure iron is an element. When iron rusts, it becomes a compound of iron oxide.

Section II Periodic Table

1. Discuss the early work of alchemists. Consult the Internet, an encyclopedia, or any other appropriate source for the history of chemistry.

2. Have your student(s) collect materials and label them according to the major components. Most substances on earth do not occur in pure elemental form; they are either in compounds or in mixtures. Only a very few are ever found in pure state unless the material has been refined.

Below are some suggestions for materials students can collect and label. They can label the major element present, even though the substance may be a mixture or a compound. Place the material on a special table for review. Be sure each one is properly labeled with the symbol of the major component. Examples:

   a. Collect a sample of copper wire and label it Cu. Note the uses of copper.
   b. Collect an old-fashioned zinc jar lid. Label it Zn and note the many uses of zinc.
   c. Collect a sample of sand. Note that one of the major components is silicon. Label the major element present as Si. Note the use of silicon in many different products today.
   d. Collect an aluminum orange juice can or soda pop can. Label it Al. Note the many uses of aluminum.
   e. Collect a small sample of graphite. It would be best to seal it in a plastic bag. Label the major element as carbon with a capital C.
   f. Collect a small sample of iron or an iron nail. Label it Fe.

Continue the procedure outlined above until you have collected a sample of most of the common elements. Have the students study their uses in the home and in industry. This will broaden their knowledge of the atomic table and the many elements. It will also facilitate learning the symbols. When all the collections have been made, label each one and place them on the table for students to quiz each other on the elements and symbols.

3. **Caution:** Warn students not to collect harmful materials. Have them construct a chart of the materials collected above. The chart could be prepared like the one suggested below:

Element	Symbol	Uses of this Element

4. Conduct a community survey on the types of radioactive materials that might be in your community. Some of the possible sources are listed below.

    a. chemical manufacturing plants that may use radioactive materials

    b. radioactive materials from testing of atomic bombs (fallout)

    c. atomic energy plants

    d. research labs that use radioactive materials

    e. radioactive materials or waste from atomic-powered submarines

    f. radioactive materials or waste from satellites

    g. hospital or medical use of radioactive materials in the treatment of cancer

You may be able to survey your community and come up with some other sources of radioactive materials. Study these sources. Find out what is done to prevent these materials from contaminating your community. Inquire how these materials are kept. Are they put in special containers? Prepare a summary of your findings. Indicate what precautions are taken for protection from these radioactive materials. Is this a danger to your community? Summarize your findings in an oral or written report.

Section III Chemical Change

1. Discuss color changes with indicators. Blue litmus turns pink in the presence of an acid. Pink litmus turns blue in the presence of a base.

2. Discuss the use of metals and nonmetals for common home use.

3. Discuss the uses of radioactive materials such as dials for clocks, the radioactive clock, cobalt treatment for cancer, and uranium for atomic energy.

4. Discuss how salts are formed by the combination of a metal such as Na, Mg, Ca, Li, chemically combined with substances such as Cl, F, Br, I. These form compounds which are salts. Examples: NaCl, KCl, LiCl, KBr, NaBr, NaF, $MgCl_2$.

5. Have the students diagram atoms. The easiest atoms to diagram, such as hydrogen, helium, and lithium, are recommended for this level. In the event you wish to cover more or give additional practice, the following atoms have been diagrammed for you. Atoms more difficult than the ones below show various valances and would require more complex explanation than could be given to a student in an introductory course.

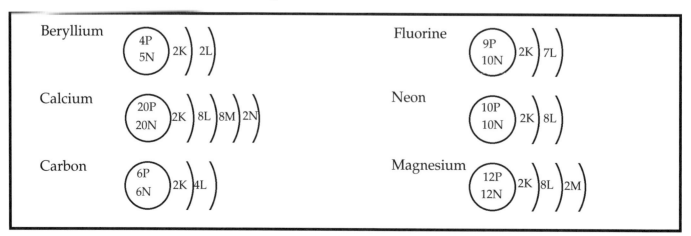

6. Perform some additional tests for acids and bases. These can be done by use of household substances the students can supply on their own. The following test solutions can be made for further student activity. Try the following solutions (indicators) on baking soda (a base) and on vinegar (an acid).

 a. Red cabbage test solution for acids and bases can be made by chopping about 5 leaves of red cabbage. Bring to a boil in 1 cup of water. Let stand 15 minutes. Drain off liquid. The liquid makes a good test solution but it has to be refrigerated. The odor becomes unbearable if not refrigerated.

 b. Another test solution can be made by mixing tumeric, an herb, in alcohol. You will find tumeric with the spices in the grocery store. Mix 1/4 cup of alcohol with 1 teaspoon of tumeric. Mix thoroughly, pour off liquid, and discard the dregs.

 c. Strong tea also makes a good indicator, although it is not as sensitive as the others.

7. Have pupils test flowers for acid-base reactions. Follow these directions:

 a. Rub a red geranium flower on a paper towel until you get a red spot. Expose the red spot on the towel to the fumes of a little household ammonia. This can be done by placing the paper towel over the top of an open bottle. The fumes will change the red spot to blue.

 b. Save the blue spot on the paper towel that you have just made with the ammonia. Expose the blue spot to a drip of vinegar. The vinegar (acid) will change the blue spot back to the red color of the geranium.

8. Study some of the rare earth elements. Consult the Internet, an encyclopedia, or a chemical handbook for information. Try to find out where they are located. Are they in rock formations? Soil? Report data and illustrate in chart form.

9. Study the use of chemical fertilizers. Find out how Ca, P, and K are added to the soil.

10. Tests for Acids and Bases

Litmus paper is paper containing an indicator solution. Blue litmus paper turns pink in the presence of an acid. Pink litmus paper turns blue in the presence of a base.

These supplies are needed:

 pink and blue litmus test papers
 1 tsp. baking soda mixed in 1 tbsp. water
 1 tsp. household ammonia mixed in 1 tbsp. water
 1 tsp. vinegar mixed in 1 tbsp. water
 1 tsp. boric acid crystals or powder mixed in 1 tbsp. hot water
 4 eyedroppers or a little plastic spoon
 1 paper plate (to put litmus paper on during the experiment)

Follow these instructions.

Before opening the litmus paper, read the instructions carefully.

1. Do not handle the litmus. Touch only the tip of the paper as you remove it from the bottle. The acidity of your hands could ruin the test.

2. Be sure to seal the containers at once. There may be fumes of acids or bases that could ruin the remaining test papers.

3. Keep the strips of test papers on the paper plate.

   a. Place two strips of blue litmus paper on the paper plate. Carefully place one drop of vinegar solution on one strip. What color did the blue litmus turn? What color did the pink litmus turn?

   b. Place one drop of boric acid solution on the other strip of litmus paper. What color did the blue litmus turn?

   c. Place two strips of pink litmus paper on the paper plate. Do not let it touch the acids you have just tested. Add a drop of baking soda solution to one strip.

   d. Put one drop of ammonia solution on the remaining strip of paper. What color did the pink litmus turn? Record your data for each of the solutions. See the example chart.

Test Solution	Litmus Paper Used	Color Reaction
baking soda	pink litmus	
ammonia	pink litmus	
vinegar	blue litmus	
boric acid	blue litmus	

   e. Test a piece of blue litmus with one of your base solutions. You should not get a color reaction. Then, test a piece of pink litmus with one of your acid solutions. You should not get a color reaction. In other words, blue litmus is supposed to turn pink in the presence of an acid but not in the presence of a base. Likewise, pink litmus is supposed to turn blue in the presence of a base but not in the presence of an acid.

Materials Needed for LIFEPAC

Required:

8 test tubes or pop bottles
piece of string, 4 feet long
crayons: red, orange, yellow, green, blue, indigo, and violet
tuning fork (you can substitute a stainless steel dinner fork)
piece of rope or clothesline about 10 feet long
approximately 10 clear plastic water glasses (disposable type)
tray or pan for making prism
inexpensive mirror for making prism
3 flashlights
food coloring (red, yellow, and blue)
red, green, and blue cellophane
1 sheet of each paper: white, black, green, and red
cardboard circle for making color wheel
coin
pencil
glue or shellac
encyclopedia
physical science texts (8th or 9th grade level)

Additional Learning Activities

Section I Waves

1. With a friend, gather materials that are transparent, translucent, and opaque. Show and display your findings.

2. With a friend, demonstrate the principle of refraction.

3. Draw and label a diagram of the ear. Explain how the ear receives sound waves. Present your findings.

4. Make a megaphone out of cardboard or plastic. How does it amplify sound?

5. Suspend a fork on a piece of cotton thread. Hold the ends of the thread against your ears, pressing your ears closed. Allow the fork to hang freely. Have someone bang the fork gently. The sound will travel through the thread to your ears.

Section II The Spectrum

1. Demonstrate the use of a prism.

2. Discuss this question with others: What is the difference between the visible spectrum and the electromagnetic spectrum?

3. With a friend, visit your local library and look up books on the spectrum. If possible, see what information is available through the Internet.

4. With a friend, make a bulletin board on the spectrum.

5. Place ice cubes in two plastic cups. wrap one cup in black cloth and one in white. Set them in the sun. Check to see which melts first. Why does this happen?

6. Prepare a chart of the electromagnetic spectrum. List something that this particular part of the spectrum does, either harmful or helpful. This is a sample chart:

Part of the Electromagnetic Spectrum	Use or Special Characteristic
radar	used to track planes and cars
A.C. power	
microwaves	
infrared	
ultraviolet light	
X-ray	
radio waves	
visible light	
gamma rays	
cosmic rays	

7. Research Sir Isaac Newton's experiments with light. Write a report on his findings.

8. Study how red light affects plants. Consult a botany book or the Internet for your research.

9. Make a bowl full of soapsuds with liquid detergent. Dip a cup into the suds and remove it gently. The bubble which forms should display a rainbow. Determine the sequence of colors in the rainbow.

Section III Colors

1. Discuss these questions with other students:

    a. If you mix yellow and blue colorants, what color will you get?

    b. Why are people concerned with color?

    c. What do we use the red light for?

    d. What does the color green mean?

    e. What are the primary colors of light? Of pigments/colorants?

2. Demonstrate a color wheel for other students.

3. With a friend, make a collage of colors. Label them as primary and secondary.

4. With a friend, set up an experiment between colors of pigment (colorants) and colors of light. Share the results of your experiment with other students.

5. Pick your favorite color. Write a one-page report on what that color means to you and why.

6. Research the psychology of colors through the Internet or at the library. Share your findings in an oral report with other students.

Materials Needed for LIFEPAC

Required:

spring scale with a hook
box weighing 3 pounds
watch with a second hand
quart jar
square piece of cardboard
marble
sand
8- x 10-inch piece lightweight,
  flexible cardboard
quart milk carton
1 piece, 6" wire
scissors
plastic board

Suggested:

encyclopedia
Bible concordance

Additional Learning Activities

Section I Definition of Force

1. Demonstrate the computation of work on the board. Have several students work at the blackboard and compute the work problems.

2. With a friend, figure out how much work you expend when you climb a stairway 10 feet high.

3. Make a poster showing how to compute work.

4. Research gravity on the Internet and/or in the library. Write a one-page report on gravity. Explain in your report what would happen on earth if there were no longer a force of gravity.

Section II Rate of Doing Work

1. With a friend, cut out or draw pictures that illustrate Newton's laws. Write the laws on a large chart and illustrate them with your pictures.

2. With a friend, visit a scientific museum. Ask about Newton's laws.

3. Write a paragraph on the difference between power and work.

Section III Change In Motion

1. With a friend, visit a machine shop. Ask about friction and its effect on the machines.

2. With a friend, make a poster illustrating different kinds of machines.

3. Write a two-page report on friction, inertia, and gravity.

4. Write a one-page report on why man needs machines.

Materials Needed for LIFEPAC

Required:

coin, such as a quarter or a half dollar
a large ball about the size of a basketball *or* a cardboard circle 8 inches diameter
a small ball about the size of a tennis ball *or* a cardboard circle 3 inches diameter
a light of about 100 watts or more
yardstick
ruler
piece of chalk
ball of string or twine
150 pennies

Additional Learning Activities

Section I Earth's Motion

1. With a friend or an adult, use a globe and light bulb to demonstrate how the sun shines on the earth.

2. With a friend, demonstrate how the angle of the sun's rays affects the amount of heat the earth gets. Fill two boxes with sand or dirt. Lay a thermometer in each box with its bulb buried about an inch deep. Set one box flat on the ground and the other on a slant. Check the temperature in each box in about ten minutes.

3. In your own words, explain why an accident could happen at 8:00 A.M. and someone in Washington, D.C., could hear about it before 4:00 A.M.

4. Write a story about what it would be like to live on a part of the earth where the sun doesn't set for months and then doesn't rise for months.

Section II Eclipses

1. Arrange a field trip to go to a local planetarium.

2. With a friend, make two posters. On one poster, make a drawing of a lunar eclipse. On the other, make a drawing of a solar eclipse.

3. Do some research on the solar eclipse. When was the last one where you live? See how many photographs you can find. Display them.

Section III The Solar System

1. With a friend, make a model of the solar system using different sized balls. Label all the planets and the sun.

2. With a friend, make a large chart that shows a comparison of the planets. Include information like diameter, distance from the sun, number of satellites, and revolution and rotation times. Display your chart in your classroom.

Independent Activities

1. Select one planet (other than earth), and write a two-page report on it.

2. Read science fiction stories about life on other planets. Could such life really exist? Explain your reason in a one-page report.

Materials Needed for LIFEPAC

Required:
  white construction paper/poster board
  coloring crayons, colored pencils, or colored markers
  cardboard cylinder from inside a roll of paper towels
  piece of plastic diffraction grating (*transmission type*)
  small ruler
  sheet of black construction paper
  scotch tape or masking tape
  pencil
  scissors
  string
  plastic protractor
  metal nut
  world map

Suggested:
  Star chart for current month and latitude location

Additional Learning Activities

Section I Astronomy

1. Visit an observatory with a friend.

2. Build your own telescope. Kits are available from scientific supply houses.

Section II Stars

1. Organize an astronomy club with your friends. Set up several star-watching sessions.

2. With a friend, make a collage space vehicle. Investigate how astronomers measure distance. Report your finds to your class.

3. Obtain a star chart for the current month and for your latitude position from the Internet or from astronomy magazines. Share them with your classmates.

Section III Constellations and Major Stars

1. With several friends, write a skit about what life would be like on another star. What would our sun look like? Present the skit in class.

2. With a friend, make several large posters of the constellations described in your LIFEPAC. Display them in your classroom.

3. Select a constellation that you have not studied yet. Research it on the Internet or library. Write a one- to two-page report on what you learned. Turn in your report to your teacher.

Materials Needed for LIFEPAC

Required:

Additional Learning Activities

Section I Plant and Animal Systems

1. Go to the library and find a video, film, or filmstrip on the main plant structures. Show it to the class.

2. With a friend, visit a botanical garden.

3. With a friend, make a chart listing and defining natural and artificial plant regulators.

4. Use the Internet or library to research the transport system of plants. Write a one-page report and share it with the class.

5. Draw and label a diagram of the human digestive system.

Section II Chemistry and Physics

1. Demonstrate that all sound is produced by vibration of air. Make an even beat and an uneven beat to distinguish between music and noise.

2. Explain the difference between pitch and amplitude. Demonstrate the difference using a musical instrument.

3. With a friend, make a chart listing the properties and examples of liquids, gases, and solids.

4. Use the Internet or library to research atoms. Write a one-page report on the structure of the atom.

5. Make a poster of the spectrum.

Section III Spaceship Earth and the Stars

1. With a friend, draw and color pictures of the different seasons. Make one chart explaining the seasons.

2. With a friend, draw a diagram of our solar system.

3. Use the Internet or library to research gravity. Write a one-page report on the importance of gravity to our planet.

4. Diagram the sun and tell its composition and source of energy.

ALTERNATE

T E S T S

Reproducible Tests
for use with the Science 600
Teacher's Guide

Name _____

Match these items (each answer, 2 points).

1. ___ chlorophyll
2. ___ light
3. ___ oxygen
4. ___ auxin
5. ___ legume
6. ___ enzyme
7. ___ glucose
8. ___ manure
9. ___ artificial
10. ___ cortex

a. sugar made during photosynthesis
b. a chemical produced in the growing tips of roots
c. green "stuff" in plants
d. storage part of root
e. energy for photosynthesis
f. natural fertilizer
g. man-made
h. by-product of photosynthesis
i. chemical used to help digestion
j. a plant which does not take nitrogen from the soil

Write the correct letter to match with the part on the line (each answer, 3 points).

11. ___ palisade layer
12. ___ stomata
13. ___ cuticle
14. ___ chloroplast
15. ___ phloem

Complete this diagram with the name of each part (each answer, 4 points).

16. _____
17. _____
18. _____
19. _____
20. _____

Write the letter of the correct answer on each line (each answer, 3 points).

21. Iodine turns _____ bluish-black.

   a. sugar   b. starch   c. fats   d. protein

22. The worst light for growing plants is _____.

    a. green   b. blue   c. orange   d. red

23. Leaves appear green because the _____ light bounces off the leaf.

    a. white   b. black   c. green   d. red

24. For plants to grow best, they must have _____.

    a. light and food
    b. oxygen and food
    c. light, food, water, and carbon dioxide
    d. air

25. Natural fertilizer is called _____ fertilizer.

    a. artificial   b. liquid   c. organic   d. spongy

26. The use of _____ indicates the presence of glucose by turning red.

    a. Benedict's solution
    b. litmus
    c. iodine
    d. alcohol

27. Water and minerals are absorbed by _____.

    a. leaves   b. stems   c. root hairs   d. cortex

28. Water and minerals are carried upward by _____.

    a. phloem   b. xylem   c. pith   d. bark

29. The gas plants need to carry on photosynthesis is _____.

    a. oxygen   b. nitrogen   c. carbon dioxide   d. methane

30. The chemical found in saliva is a(n) _____.

    a. legume   b. bacteria   c. starch   d. enzyme

Complete these activities (each answer, 3 points).

31. List three ways plants regulate growth naturally.

    a. _____.
    b. _____.
    c. _____.

32. Name two advantages of using artificial regulators.

    a. _____.
    b. _____.

Date _____

Score _____

Possible Score _____ **100** _____

50

Name _____

Write the name of the body part on the line by the number (each answer, 2 points).

1. _____
2. _____
3. _____
4. _____
5. _____
6. _____

1

2

3

4

5

6

Match these items (each answer, 2 points).

7. ___ alimentary canal   a. source of rennin

8. ___ mouth   b. source of saliva

9. ___ stomach   c. parts of the body through which food passes

10. ___ liver   d. makes bile

                               e. excretes waste

Write *true* **or** *false* (each answer, 1 point).

11. _____ Arteries carry blood away from the heart.

12. _____ Capillaries are thick, close-to-the-surface tubes that appear blue.

13. _____ The red cells of the blood contain hemoglobin.

14. _____ Anemia is caused by too much iron.

15. _____ Blood type AB is called a "universal donor".

Complete these statements (each answer, 3 points).

16. Incisors are designed to help us a. _____ our food, and molars help us b. _____ our food.

17. Two body parts that produce digestive juices necessary to finish digestion of food are a. _____ and b. _____.

18. Two preventatives for skin and kidney disease are a. _____ and b. _____.

19. The lower chamber of the heart is the _____.

20. A heart murmur is caused by incorrect operation of _____.

Complete this list (each answer, 3 points).

21. List three major bones of the body.

    a. _____

    b. _____

    c. _____

Complete these statements (each answer, 3 points).

22. The heart muscle is an example of a _____ type muscle.

23. The muscle found around the stomach is an example of a _____ type muscle.

24. The biceps are an example of a _____ type muscle.

Match these items. Answers may be used more than once (each answer, 2 points).

25. a. ___ purposes of the skin   a. fight infection

    b. ___   b. exercises

26. a. ___ ways to keep bones healthy   c. purifies

    b. ___   d. bulky foods

27. ___ purpose of red cells   e. protects

28. ___ prevents cancer of colon   f. cools

29. a. ___ purpose of skeletal system   g. makes marrow

    b. ___   h. senses

30. ___ purpose of white cells   i. proper diet

                                         j. carry oxygen and carbon dioxide

Complete these activities (each answer, 3 points).

31. List and describe two causes of lung disease.

    a. _____

    b. _____

32. List three diseases of the muscle and skeletal systems.

    a. _____

    b. _____

    c. _____

Date _____

Score _____

Possible Score _____ 100 _____

Name _____

Match these items (each answer, 2 points).

1. ___ bird flying south for the winter
2. ___ ecological group of plants and animals
3. ___ earth to life to earth
4. ___ controls our muscle coordination
5. ___ name of your nerve cells
6. ___ blinking your eye
7. ___ close living relationship
8. ___ combing your hair daily
9. ___ the spot where nerve cells pass on messages
10. ___ sending end of nerve cells
11. ___ receiving end of nerve cells
12. ___ front part of the brain
13. ___ grass rabbit fox
14. ___ growth of plants due to an environmental stimulus
15. ___ controls reflexes

a. tropism
b. cycle
c. medulla
d. symbiosis
e. food chain
f. biome
g. cerebrum
h. cerebellum
i. reflex
j. instinct
k. habit
l. neurons
m. axon
n. dendrite
o. synapse

Write the correct letter and answer on each line (each answer, 2 points).

16. The tropism that causes plants to grow toward the earth is _____.
    a. geotropism   b. hydrotropism   c. phototropism   d. heliotropism

17. Plant growth that causes plants to grow toward sunlight is _____.
    a. geotropism   b. phototropism   c. hydrotropism   d. heliotropism

18. It controls instant messages to prevent burns and injury. _____.
    a. synapse   b. axon   c. spinal cord   d. dendrite

19. Bundles of nerves collect near the spinal column and are called _____.
    a. dendrites   b. axons   c. synapse   d. plexus

20. The biome nearest the equator is the _____.
    a. tundra   b. tropical forest   c. grassland   d. desert

Complete these statements (each answer, 3 points).

21. The driest biome is a(n) _____.

22. The chemical causing a tropism is _____.

23. The ganglia is _____.

24. The most advanced of all creatures is _____.

25. The function of the cortex of the brain is to _____
    _____.

26. A cycle is a(n)_____
    _____
    _____.

27. An example of an aquatic biome is_____
    _____

28. A reflex is a(n) _____.

29. Built-in consciousness is called _____.

30. *Trial and error* can be defined as _____
    _____
    _____.

Match the following items Answers may be used more than once (each answer, 2 points).

31. ___ reason   a. medulla

32. ___ makes sense out of sensory information   b. cerebellum

33. ___ controls muscle coordination   c. cerebrum

34. ___ controls motor senses

35. ___ controls reflexes

Complete the following activity (each answer, 2 points).

36. Put the following organisms into a food chain and identify each as a *producer, con-sumer,* or *decomposer.* (bacteria, seed, lion, weasel, bird)

Organism	Function
a. _____	f. _____
b. _____	g. _____
c. _____	h. _____
d. _____	i. _____
e. _____	j. _____

Date _____
Score _____
Possible Score _____ 100

Name _____

Answer these questions (each answer, 5 points).

1. How do we get seedless navel oranges? _____
_____

2. What do we know about DNA and mutations that is contrary to the theory of evolution?
_____
_____
_____
_____

3. What is one main feature of DNA? _____
_____

4. How are mutations in plants helpful to man in providing food? List some examples.
_____
_____

5. How may foods or temperature interact with genes? _____
_____
_____

Match these items (each answer, 3 points).

6. ___ a female reproductive cell
7. ___ a male reproductive cell
8. ___ the name of a gene which does not produce its effect when an opposite dominant gene is present
9. ___ the powdery substance found on the anthers of a flower
10. ___ the kind of cell division which replaces old cells
11. ___ the science of heredity
12. ___ genes that control heredity
13. ___ the substance that is removed from ribose in the DNA molecule
14. ___ the kind of cell division that reduces the chromosome number
15. ___ a substance lacking in albino plants

a. harmful
b. reduction division
c. pollen
d. egg
e. oxygen
f. sperm
g. genetics
h. recessive
i. multiple
j. mitosis
k. chlorophyll

Write *true* **or** *false* (each answer, 1 point).

16. _____ The receptacle holds the flower.
17. _____ When yellow peas are crossed with green peas, the first generation is yellow.

18. _____ If a nontaster married a nontaster, the first generation would all have to be nontasters.

19. _____ Genes may interact with the environment to produce an altered effect.

20. _____ If a purebred tall pea is crossed with a purebred dwarf pea, the first generation would all be tall.

21. _____ If a nontaster marries a taster, you would expect some children to be tasters.

22. _____ Mutations are fairly common.

23. _____ Mutations are rarely harmful.

24. _____ Oxygen is the substance removed from deoxyribonucleic acid.

25. _____ A change in gene results in a changed trait.

Write the correct letter and answer on each line (each answer, 3 points).

26. A condition where neither gene dominates the other is known as

    _____.

    a. a recessive condition   b. a dominant condition   c. incomplete dominance

27. A characteristic carried by a gene is _____.
    a. a trait   b. a mutation   c. purebred

28. A transfer of pollen from the anther of one flower to the stigma of another is

    _____.

    a. fertilization   b. cross-pollination   c. self-pollination

29. The resulting offspring from a cross between two individuals differing in one or more genes is a _____.
    a. purebred   b. mutation   c. hybrid

30. In a garden pea whose chromosome number is 14, reduction division would produce _____.
    a. new cells with the same number of chromosomes
    b. new cells with half the number of chromosomes
    c. cells exactly like the original cell in every respect

Complete these activities (each answer, 4 points).

31. Name three parts of a flower.

    a. _____   b. _____   c. _____

32. Describe two ways in which many living organisms have variation.

    a. _____

    _____

    b. _____

    _____

Date _____

Score _____

Possible Score _____ 100 _____

Name _____

Match these items (each answer, 3 points).

1. ___ the measurement of the pull of gravity on an object or body

2. ___ the amount of matter in a body or object

3. ___ a pure substance that can't be broken down into a simpler substance

4. ___ all of the elements to the left of the stair steps on the periodic chart

5. ___ the smallest particle of an element

6. ___ a base indicator

7. ___ a compound of copper and iodine

8. ___ a plus-charged particle in an atomic nucleus

9. ___ a substance that gives off powerful rays or fast-moving charged particles

10. ___ elements with atomic numbers above 92

a. mass
b. man-made
c. radioactive substance
d. weight
e. element

f. proton

g. atom

h. phenolphthalein

i. copper iodide

j. metals

k. carbon dioxide

Write *true* **or** *false* (each answer, 1 point).

11. _____ The weight of an atom is the protons and neutrons added together.

12. _____ An electron is so tiny that its weight is not important.

13. _____ A neutron always has a plus electrical charge.

14. _____ A liquid has a fixed shape that can't be changed.

15. _____ An object may be weightless in space but have the same mass.

16. _____ Metals are known for their ability to conduct heat and electricity.

17. _____ H_2O is the formula for water.

18. _____ Baking soda is a base.

19. _____ Citric acid is found in oranges, grapefruit, and limes.

20. _____ There are at least 287 elements which occur in nature.

Write the chemical symbol for the elements listed below (each answer, 2 points).

21. hydrogen ___

22. calcium ___

23. chlorine ___

24. magnesium ___

25. zinc ___

26. silver ___

27. iodine ___

28. sulfur ___

29. silicon ___   31. iron ___

30. phosphorus ___   32. helium ___

Write the correct letter and answer on each line (each answer, 2 points).

33.   Air is an example of the state of matter known as _____.

    a. solid   b. liquid   c. gas

34.   A solid has a _____.

    a. shape that changes with the container

    b. shape that is readily changed

    c. fixed shape

35.   An atom is the smallest particle of _____.

    a. a compound

    b. an element

    c. the compound copper iodide

36.   A liquid has _____.

    a. a fixed shape

    b. the shape of the container

    c. a shape that can never be changed

37.   Steam is an example of a _____.

    a. solid   b. liquid   c. gas

38.   The atomic number tells the _____.

    a. number of protons

    b. number of neutrons

    c. chemical symbol

39.   Atomic weight is _____.

    a. the neutrons multiplied by the protons

    b. the electrons and protons added together

    c. protons plus neutrons

40.   Vinegar contains a weak acid known as _____ acid.

    a. citric   b. boric   c. acetic

Complete these activities (each answer, 2 points).

41.   What is an electron cloud model?

    _____

    _____.

42. Tell what each of these means on the periodic chart in relation to nitrogen.

    a. 7 _____

    b. N _____

    c. 14 _____

43. Why is it easy to combine sodium (Na) with chlorine (Cl), two elements that are poisonous to animals and man, to form table salt, a harmless compound with which we season our food? _____

    _____

    _____.

44. Three kinds of particles in an atom are

    a. _____

    b. _____

    c. _____

45. The lightest element known is _____.

46. The atomic weight is a weight compared to the element _____.

Date _____

Score _____

Possible Score _____ 100 _____

Science 606 Alternate Test

Name _____

Answer *true* **or** *false* (each answer, 1 point).

1. _____ The rainbow and spectrum have the same colors.

2. _____ Violet is the shortest color wave.

3. _____ Another word for throwing back or turning back is *reflect*.

4. _____ The color produced when all pigments are mixed is black.

5. _____ Red glass lets only red light pass through.

6. _____ Either a prism or a water droplet can refract light.

7. _____ Newton used water to separate the colors of light.

8. _____ When green and red lights are mixed, the color violet is produced.

Complete these statements (each answer, 3 points).

9. The speed of light is _____ miles per second.

10. The speed of sound is _____ feet per second.

11. The top of a light wave is called a _____.

12. The bottom of a light wave is called a _____.

13. Sound is produced by vibrations of _____ molecules.

14. Sound travels _____ than light.

15. A kind of material that light cannot go through is _____.

16. Visible and invisible light is called the _____.

17. The longest visible part of the visible spectrum is the color _____.

18. The shortest part of the visible spectrum is the color _____.

19. An invisible form of radiation is _____.

20. The electromagnetic spectrum is _____
_____ _____.

21. The fact that white light is composed of colors was discovered by _____.

22. The absolute absence of all light is called _____.

23. The band of colors that makes up light is called the _____.

24. The primary colors of pigments are a. _____, b. _____,
and c. _____.

25. The primary colors of light are a. _____, b. _____, and
c. _____.

26. When all colors are absorbed you can see only _____.

27. The word *absorb* means _____.

28. The mixing of yellow and blue pigments produces _____.

Match these items (each answer, 2 points).

29. ____ the pushing together of molecules in a sound wave

30. ____ the thinning of air molecules in a sound wave

31. ____ vibrate when sound waves are received

32. ____ collects sound waves

33. ____ a material that will allow some light to pass through

34. ____ a clear material that allows light to pass through

35. ____ sound waves pass rapidly through this material; they move faster than in air

36. ____ all of the visible and invisible radiations received by planet earth

37. ____ triangular solid used to separate colors

38. ____ reflects all colors

a. pitch

b. rarefaction

c. white

d. prism

e. compression

f. transparent

g. electromagnetic spectrum

h. translucent

i. external ear

j. ear bones

k. steel

l. amplitude

Date _____

Score _____

Possible Score _____100_____

Science 607 Alternate Test

Name _____

Match each item (each answer, 2 points).

1. ____ a force that opposes motion
2. ____ the force that pulls things toward the center of the earth
3. ____ a metric measure of work
4. ____ force used to generate electricity
5. ____ a push or pull action
6. ____ the rate of doing work
7. ____ the measurement of electric power
8. ____ the product of force moving through a distance
9. ____ the tendency of an object to remain at rest or to continue motion in a straight line with constant speed
10. ____ a mechanical device people use to do work

a. kilogram-meter
b. work
c. force
d. power
e. gravity
f. motion
g. watt
h. inertia
i. machine
j. friction
k. muscular

Write *true* **or** *false* (each answer, 1 point).

11. _____ All things in the universe move.
12. _____ Gravity pulls things away from the earth.
13. _____ More force is required to pull an object than to lift it.
14. _____ *Work* is defined as the *spending of energy*.
15. _____ All forces produce motion.
16. _____ Objects at rest tend to stay at rest unless acted upon by a force.
17. _____ Machines decrease the amount of work to be done.
18. _____ The work put into a machine is equal to the work coming out of a machine, provided inertia and friction are so small they are disregarded.
19. _____ You wear a seat belt in a car because of gravity.
20. _____ The moon stays in orbit because of inertia.
21. _____ Machines are used to move things.
22. _____ The work principle is always true.
23. _____ Machines can change motion.
24. _____ Friction is a force that opposes motion.
25. _____ Work *in* equals work *out*.

Match the event with the correct cause (each answer, 2 points).

26. ____ You dropped a package on the ground.   a. inertia

27. ____ You skidded on a wet sidewalk.   b. gravity

28. ____ You couldn't stop your skateboard at the corner; c. friction
    it kept moving.

29. ____ You threw a frisbee and it broke a window and   d. loss of friction
    knocked over a lamp.

30. ____ A force keeps Mars in orbit.

31. ____ You were late getting to school because the
    roads were icy.

32. ____ A force causes part of the machinery to wear
    out when they touch each other.

33. ____ When you rub your hands together, they
    get warm.

34. ____ You drop a ball on a hill and it keeps rolling
    until it hits the flat bottom of the hill.

35. ____ You slip on a banana peel and fall.

Complete these statements (each answer, 3 points).

36. Horsepower is the unit used for measuring _____.

37. The watt is a unit of _____.

38. Work is done only when an object is moved by a(n) _____.

39. A metric unit for measuring work is called the _____.

40. Work is measured by multiplying the force by _____.

41. The continuing forward movement of your body in a car after it stops is due to

    _____.

42. Friction is a force that opposes _____.

43. Power is the speed or rate of doing _____.

44. *Force* is defined as _____.

45. More force is required to lift an object than to push it along a smooth surface
    because of _____.

Complete these activities (each answer, 5 points).

46. Briefly summarize the law of inertia. _____

    _____

47. Briefly summarize the law of gravity _____

     _____

     _____

     _____

48. How do machines change motion? _____

     _____

     _____

Date _____

Score _____

Possible Score _____ **100** _____

Name _____

Match each item (each answer, 2 points).

1. ____ an eclipse in which the moon is darkened
2. ____ an eclipse in which the sun is darkened
3. ____ the lightest, outer edges of a shadow
4. ____ a law that pertains to heavenly bodies being attracted to one another
5. ____ a shooting star
6. ____ a planet with rings
7. ____ the most distant planet
8. ____ a planet with no moons
9. ____ the star closest to Earth
10. ____ the sun's energy
11. ____ the water planet

a. an asteroid
b. nuclear fusion
c. Earth
d. lunar eclipse
e. solar eclipse
f. meteor
g. Neptune
h. Venus
i. penumbra
j. gravitation
k. Saturn
l. the sun

Write *true* **or** *false* (each answer, 1 point).

12. _____ The earth is about 93,000,000 miles from the sun.
13. _____ The whole earth is darkened during a total eclipse.
14. _____ Most asteroids are located between Mars and Jupiter.
15. _____ A solar day is longer than a sidereal day.
16. _____ Jupiter is the largest planet in our solar system.
17. _____ The South Pole has six months of darkness.

Complete these statements (each answer, 3 points).

18. Days and nights are equal during the _____.
19. A *shooting star* that hits the earth is called a _____ _____.
20. The diameter of the earth at the poles is about _____ miles.
21. Earth is a very special place because it has a. _____ and b. _____.
22. Our solar system contains _____ planets.
23. People within the penumbra see a _____ eclipse of the sun.
24. The earth is tilted on its axis about _____.
25. During a _____ eclipse, the earth is darkened because the moon comes between the earth and the sun.

26. The sun appears to rise in the east and set in the west because of _____

_____

_____.

27. If the earth were not tilted, the days and nights would be _____.

28. The two laws concerning gravitation and inertia were proposed by _____

_____.

29. The seasons are caused by the earth's tilt and its _____.

30. Objects in our solar system that have a coma and tail are called _____.

31. A _____ is a dust or small particle in space that becomes a shooting star when it enters earth's atmosphere.

32. The temperature on the surface of the sun is about _____.

Complete these activities (each answer, 3 points).

33. What causes a total eclipse of the sun?

_____

_____

34. Three types of motion of spaceship earth are:

a. _____

b. _____

c. _____

35. How are the vernal equinox and the autumnal equinox the same?

_____

_____

36. Name the first three planets outward from the sun in their proper order.

a. _____

b. _____

c. _____

Date _____

Score _____

Possible Score _____ 100 _____

Name _____

Match each item (each answer, 2 points).

1. _____ source of sun's energy
2. _____ Great Bear constellation
3. _____ power plant of the sun
4. _____ example of red star
5. _____ example of yellow star
6. _____ southern lights
7. _____ person who discovered radio waves from outer space
8. _____ name of the dark lines in the spectrum
9. _____ inventor of telescope
10. _____ distance light travels in one year, used as a measurement for star distances
11. _____ example of a white dwarf star
12. _____ sometimes, it is the planet farthest from sun
13. _____ constellation in which Polaris is located
14. _____ third planet from the sun
15. _____ instrument used to observe a spectrum

a. sun
b. spectroscope
c. Earth
d. nuclear fusion
e. Ursa Major
f. central core
g. Betelgeuse
h. Aurora Australis
i. Jansky
j. Lippershey
k. Fraunhofer
l. one light-year
m. companion to Sirius
n. Neptune
o. Ursa Minor

Write *true* **or** *false* (each answer, 1 point).

16. _____ Galileo made the first telescope for astronomy.
17. _____ All of Galileo's observations were made from a refracting telescope.
18. _____ Fraunhofer lines are dark lines in the spectrum.
19. _____ The smallest stars are white dwarfs.
20. _____ The Great Bear constellation is known as Ursa Minor.
21. _____ Galileo observed sunspots.
22. _____ The planet Mercury is closest to the sun.
23. _____ A spectroscope is useful in studying the spectra of stars.
24. _____ The photosphere is the halo around the sun which is seen during an eclipse.
25. _____ Our solar system is located in the center of the Milky Way.
26. _____ Cassiopeia is shaped like a giant *W* or *M*.

Complete these statements (each answer, 3 points).

27. Rigel is located in the constellation _____.

28. One way stars differ is in _____.

29. A light-year is approximately _____ trillion miles.

30. Polaris is located in the constellation known as Ursa _____.

31. An astronomical unit consists of _____.

32. A diffraction grating is _____
     _____.

33. Betelgeuse is located in the constellation _____.

34. Einstein developed important theories of _____.

35. The constellation known as the Herdsman is called _____.

36. The fourth planet from the sun outward is _____.

37. Our sun consists of 99 per cent helium and _____ gases.

38. The name of a cluster of stars is _____ (you have studied two).

39. The northern and southern lights are believed to be caused by
     _____
     _____.

Answer these questions (each answer, 5 points).

40. If you were lost, how might you find your way home at night?
     _____
     _____

41. How was helium discovered? _____
     _____
     _____

42. What two things has the Lord been able to do concerning the stars that man has
     never been able to do? (The answer lies in Psalm 147:4.) _____ ____
     _____
     _____

43. Why did God create all things?
     _____
     _____

Date _____

Score _____

Possible Score _____ 100

Name _____

Match each item (each answer, 2 points).

1. ____ sending end of a neuron
2. ____ front part of brain
3. ____ tubes in plants
4. ____ unit for measuring power of engines
5. ____ lightest part of a shadow
6. ____ clear, allows light to pass through
7. ____ ring of light just above the sun's surface
8. ____ highness or lowness of a sound
9. ____ spongy center layer of bone
10. ____ darkest part of a shadow
11. ____ thin or far apart
12. ____ period of year when days and nights are equal
13. ____ product of force moving through a distance
14. ____ anything that has mass and occupies space
15. ____ iron compound in red blood cells
16. ____ plant growth caused by some outside stimulus
17. ____ outer layer of cells
18. ____ a nerve cell

a. horsepower
b. marrow
c. transparent
d. axon
e. xylem
f. hemoglobin
g. brain stem
h. tropism
i. cerebrum
j. pitch
k. penumbra
l. matter
m. work
n. rarefaction
o. corona
p. umbra
q. neuron
r. equinox
s. epidermis

Write *true* **or** *false* (each answer, 1 point).

19. _____ Photosynthesis is the food-making process in green plants.
20. _____ Black reflects light.
21. _____ The human body has 210 bones.
22. _____ A rainbow is white light that has been refracted by raindrops.
23. _____ The energy for photosynthesis comes from the sun.
24. _____ Sound waves can travel through liquids and gases, but not solids.
25. _____ The bladder is the body's storage area for liquid wastes.
26. _____ Atoms are so small that they cannot be identified by X-ray.
27. _____ The loudness of a sound is its amplitude.
28. _____ An important by-product of photosynthesis is carbon dioxide.
29. _____ Biomes occurring in water are called aquatic biomes.

Complete this activity (each answer, 1 point).

30. Write the element's name after each symbol.

 a. He _____   d. S _____

 b. Na _____   e. Ca _____

 c. Cl _____   f. Fe _____

Complete these statements (each answer, 3 points).

31. The three states of matter are a. _____, b. _____, and c. _____.

32. The system of comparing atomic weights is called relative _____.

33. One-half the distance around the world at 180° is found the International _____.

34. An ellipse is a(n) _____ - shaped orbit.

35. When the earth passes between the sun and the moon a lunar _____ occurs.

36. An asteroid resembles a small _____.

37. The sun is composed of hydrogen and _____ gases.

Complete these activities (each answer, 5 points).

38. Briefly tell the difference between a voluntary and involuntary muscle.

 _____

 _____

 _____

39. Briefly tell the function of the lungs.

 _____

 _____

 _____

 _____

40. Briefly describe a tropical rain forest biome.

 _____

 _____

 _____

41. Briefly describe the function of the cerebellum

 _____

 _____

 _____

Date _____

Score _____

Possible Score _____ 100 _____

ANSWER KEYS

SECTION ONE

1.1 The water level in both tubes dropped. The one in the light dropped more than the one in the dark

1.2 yes

1.3 the one in the light

1.4 light

1.5 amount of light

1.6 chloroplasts

1.7 palisade

1.8 top

1.9 As follows:

Seeds in dark		
Date	**Wet Seed**	**Dry Seed**
1	no change in size	no change
3	seed larger	no change
5	root and stem have begun to grow	no change
7	root and stem about 4 cm long	no change
9	root and stem about 8 cm long; root white; stem white	no change
11	root and stem about 10 cm long; root and stem white	no change

Seeds in sun		
Date	**Wet Seed**	**Dry Seed**
1	no change	no change
3	seed larger in size	no change
5	root and stem have begun to grow	no change
7	root and stem about 4 cm long;	no change
9	root and stem about 9 cm long; root white; stem green.	no change
11	root and stem about 12 cm long; root white; stem green.	no change

1.10 wet

1.11 sunlight

1.12 Any order:
a. water
b. sunlight

1.13 sunlight

1.14 those in sunlight

1.15 sunlight

1.16 sunlight

1.17 palisade

1.18 top

1.19 The top of the leaf will get more sunshine. The bottom of the leaf will be in the shade (dark).

1.20 **(Across)** **(Down)**

(Across)	(Down)
1. chloroplast	1. complex
6. life	2. root
7. plants	3. animal
9. algae	4. tree
11. energy	5. made or gave
	8. say
	10. God

1.21 **Record of Results**

blue

yellow

orange or green

red

1.22 b. decreased

1.23 a. blue to red

1.24 a. glucose increased

1.25 b

1.26 a

1.27 d

1.28 e

1.29 c

1.30 right (red)

1.31 left (green)

1.32 red

1.33 red

1.34 red

1.35 Because the leaf soaks up the rest of the colors. The green color bounces back so we can see it.

1.36 Because all that light bounces off and the leaf doesn't have any sunlight to use in photosynthesis.

1.37 Any order:
a. temperature
b. amount of sunshine
c. amount of rain (moisture)

1.38 Natural fertilizers that come from living things are called organic fertilizers.

1.39 d

1.40 a

1.41 e

1.42 b

1.43 f

1.44 c

SECTION TWO

2.1 Hint: Look for detail and specifics.

2.2 Hint: Detail is important.

2.3 Stress accuracy and detail. Does it "really" look as it is drawn.

2.4 Nearer the tip end.

2.5 Yes. This is so the greatest amount of water and minerals will be able to be taken into the root. (Should get at concept of increased surface area.)

2.6 Look for details.

2.7 They spread out in the soil to take in water and minerals and to anchor the plant in the soil.

2.8 xylem

2.9 phloem

2.10 cortex

2.11

Time	Observation
15 min.	The food coloring has moved up the stalk about 3 cm. The coloring is in streaks. The whole stalk is not colored.
30 min.	The coloring has moved up about 15 cm.
24 hrs.	The coloring has moved all the way up into the leaves. The color has concentrated at the leaf ends.

2.12 Answers will vary. Probably will include the stringy nature of the celery.

2.13 a. red or blue (whichever you use)

b. They are the only parts that show the food coloring.

2.14 red or blue (whichever you use) at tip

2.15 The food coloring had moved all the way up the stem into the leaves.

2.16 Teacher/Adult check

SECTION THREE

3.1 Record of observations of stem in water

Date	Observations
1	No change.
3	No change.
5	White bumps begin to show at the cut on the stem.
7	Roots appear to be growing on the stem.
9	Roots are about 2-5 mm long. Several are now visible.

3.2 It starts to grow roots.

3.3 yes

3.4 The stem produced chemicals to start the roots growing.

3.5 Use gibberellin.

3.6 Place the stem in water.

3.7 a. nongreen

b. abnormal

c. nonflowering

d. misuse

e. nontoxic

f. nonrigid

g. misinterpret

h. nonprotective

i. misplant

3.8 2, 4-D

3.9 cancer, liver decay, or disease

3.10 Examples: oats, soybeans, beets

3.11 Examples: Farmers and gardeners use chemical regulators to control harmful weeds in their crops.

3.12 Example: Some chemical regulators are harmful to man. Some chemical regulators pollute the soil and atmosphere.

SECTION ONE

1.1 It breaks down the food we eat into simple chemicals which can dissolve in water and pass through cell walls.

1.2 The food we eat gives us energy and nutrients needed for each cell to live.

Digestion breaks large chemicals into small, simple ones.

1.3 a. mouth

b. esophagus

c. stomach

d. small intestine

e. large intestine

f. rectum

1.4 Saliva contains an enzyme that breaks the starch down into sugar.

1.5 Hint: Look for complete sentences, detail, and accurate drawing that is properly labeled. Look for some depth of information.

1.6 Choices will vary

1.7 The milk and junket curdles and gets lumpy. It appears to get chunky.

1.8 The rennin in the stomach will digest the milk and make it lumpy.

1.9 Example: Rennin is found in the stomachs of humans and milk-feeding animals. Rennin is necessary to digest protein in the milk. If rennin were not present, babies would not be able to digest milk and could die of starvation due to lack of protein.

1.10 Oil and water do not mix. The oil forms little beads in the water and then floats to the top.

1.11 The soap makes suds, and the oil seems to have dissolved. The oil does not float to the top.

1.12 When the oil is in many little drops, it is easier for it to react than when it is in one big drop. More surface area is exposed to react.

1.13 Soap causes the oil and dirt to form an emulsion and wash off our bodies.

1.14 a. The test tape turns dark green where touched with the solution outside the bottle.

b. green

c. yes

1.15 a. The test tape turned green when touched to the solution in the bottle.

b. green

c. yes

d. The sugar passed through the porous plastic wrap.

1.16 a. There is no observable change.

b. no

1.17 a. The solution turned bluish-black.

b. bluish-black

c. yes

1.18 These two tests show that sugar can pass through the membrane while starch cannot. This probably means that sugar molecules are smaller than starch molecules.

1.19 Either order:

a. take out excess water

b. collect undigested food, bacteria, and disease organisms for excretion

1.20 Examples:

infection which causes diarrhea

cancer caused by a poor diet or lack of exercise

1.21 Teacher/Adult check

SECTION TWO

2.1   variable (approximately 70)

2.2   approximately 60

2.3   approximately 100

2.4   Answers may vary

normal: about 70

resting: about 60

jogging: about 100

2.5   The answers may vary but should be consistent with the data.

2.6   a. large vein from upper and lower halves of the body
       b. right atrium
       c. right ventricle
       d. through valve to artery
       e. artery to lungs
       f. veins from lungs
       g. left atrium
       h. left ventricle
       i. through valve
       j. aorta

2.7   Hint: Include heart to arteries to capillaries to veins to heart

2.8   arteries = thick-walled, soft, spongy, oxygen-carrying

veins = thin walls, stiffer than arteries, less strong, contain valves, waste-carrying

capillaries = single-celled walls, exchange food and oxygen for all waste, connect arteries and veins

2.9   Type O blood can be given to all other types.

2.10   Type AB can accept or receive all other blood types without rejection.

2.11   Any order:
       a. fight germs
       b. carry oxygen
       c. carry food
       d. carry waste from cells

2.12   Any order:
       a. Red cells carry food, oxygen, and wastes.
       b. White cells attack infection.
       or Platelets clot blood after the skin is cut.

2.13   Blood is essential for life to occur. Without healthy blood, the body will suffer. Healthy blood means a healthy body, generally.

2.14   a. red cells–carry oxygen and carbon dioxide
       b. white cells–fight germs
       c. platelets–clot blood

2.15   1,861,141

2.16   886,765

2.17   539,577

2.18   Diseases of Heart and Blood Vessels

2.19   The limewater turned very cloudy in about 15 minutes.

2.20   The limewater turned slightly cloudy after about one minute.

2.21   a. blowing
       b. blowing
       c. The blood carried carbon dioxide to the lungs where it was exchanged with oxygen. The waste, carbon dioxide, was breathed out.
       d. Plants consume carbon dioxide as parts of photosynthesis.

2.22 a. mouth or nose

  b. throat

  c. trachea or windpipe

  d. lungs

  e. air sacs

2.23 Any order:

  a. tuberculosis

  b. black lung

  c. emphysema or lung cancer

2.24 Any order:

  a. pollution

  b. job environment

  c. smoking

2.25 The lungs clean the waste, carbon dioxide, from the blood and add oxygen.

2.26 alcohol

2.27 alcohol

2.28 Evaporation of a liquid from your arm causes cooling. Therefore, sweating will allow evaporation to occur and cool the body.

2.29 Any order:

  a. excretes waste

  b. cools the body

  c. protects from infections

  d. has nerve cells for feeling

2.30 Any order:

  a. epidermis

  b. dead layer

  c. perspiration pore

  d. oil gland

  e. fat cells

  f. erector muscle

  g. hair shaft

2.31 Examples:

  cancer and allergies–medical attention acne and blackheads–cleanliness with soap and water

2.32 The kidneys remove liquid waste from the blood.

2.33 Harm can be done to the kidneys by eating too much protein, drinking too little liquids, and drinking alcohol.

2.34 The keys are cleanliness, proper diet, and plenty of fluids.

SECTION THREE

3.1 a. Striated muscles appear to be striped and in long fibers. Striated muscles are found in the legs, arms, and trunk. They are voluntary muscles.

  b. Smooth muscles are spindle-shaped and are not striped. Smooth muscles are in the stomach, intestines, and blood vessels. They are involuntary muscles.

  c. Cardiac muscles are striped and are grouped in a network. Cardiac muscles are in the heart. They are involuntary muscles.

3.2 Voluntary muscles are controlled by a specific thought while involuntary muscles act with no conscious thought.

3.3

a deltoid	a triceps
a sartorius	b intestine
c heart	b veins
a biceps	a trapezius
b stomach	a gastrocnemius

3.4 adult check

3.5 Any order:
   a. knee
   b. elbow
   c. toes or fingers

3.6 Either order:
   a. hip
   b. shoulder

3.7 a. head on the spine

3.8 a. vertebrae

3.9 Any order:
   a. The bones give shape to the muscles.
   b. The bones provide internal protection of the body.
   c. The interior of bones produces white and red blood cells.
   d. Bones also store calcium and phosphorus for later use.

3.10 a. carpals   b. d

3.11 a. clavicle   b. f

3.12 a. cranium   b. a

3.13 a. femur   b. c

3.14 a. fibula   b. c

3.15 a. humerus   b. b

3.16 a. ilium   b. h

3.17 a. metacarpals b. d

3.18 a. metatarsals b. e

3.19 a. patella   b. c

3.20 a. phalanges   b. d, e

3.21 a. radius   b. b

3.22 a. ribs   b. f

3.23 a. scapula   b. f

3.24 a. sternum   b. f

3.25 a. tarsals   b. e

3.26 a. tibia   b. c

3.27 a. ulna   b. b

3.28 a. vertebrae   b. g

3.29 helper check

3.30 Examples: any order:
   a. muscular dystrophy   a. cancer
   b. some forms of rheumatism   b. rickets
   c. rabies, lockjaw   c. osteomyelitis

3.31 The best medicine is a good, balanced diet and plenty of exercise.

3.32 We need to take care of our bodies so we can remain healthy and productive.

SECTION ONE

1.1   b. behavior

1.2   d. environments

1.3   a. nervous system

1.4   c. Vertebrates

1.5   b. human beings

1.6   true

1.7   true

1.8   false

1.9   false

1.10   true

1.11   Any order:

    a. cerebrum

    b. cerebellum

    c. brain stem

1.12   a. neurons

    b. glia

1.13   a. cerebrum

    b. cerebellum

    c. brain stem

    d. frontal lobe

    e. temporal lobe

    f. parietal lobe

    g. occipital lobe

    h. loft cerebral hemisphere

    i. right cerebral hemisphere

    j. longitudinal fissure

1.14   brain stem

1.15   nerve bundles

1.16   a

1.17   c

1.18   e

1.19   g

1.20   f

1.21   a

1.22   b

1.23   a

1.24   a

1.25   d

1.26   j

1.27   i

1.28   h

1.29   i

1.30   h

1.31   Any order:

    a. One function of the spinal cord is to carry nerve messages from various body parts to the brain.

    b. A second function of the spinal cord is to intercept and interpret danger signals from various parts of the body.

1.32   Tiny chemical reactions occur that excite the neurons. These trigger tiny electric signals that can be generated, transmitted, and received by the neurons. These impulses are transmitted rapidly from neuron to neuron until a message gets to the spinal cord or brain for coding or decoding. Then, an action message is sent back along another neuron to a neuron pathway.

1.33   a. axons

    b. dendrites

1.34   Teacher/Adult check

1.35   a. receive and send nerve impulses, make proteins, and use energy for growth and maintenance of nerve cell

      b. carry and transmit messages

      c. receive impulses (mostly from the axon of another neuron)

1.36   c. autonomic nervous system

1.37   a. breathing, digestion, heartbeat

1.38   c. ganglia

1.39   b. external senses

1.40   d. parasympathetic system

1.41   c. solar plexus

1.42   b. speed up

1.43   Teacher/Adult check

1.44   true

1.45   false

1.46   false

1.47   true

1.48   true

1.49   false

1.50   true

1.51   false

1.52   true

1.53   Teacher/Adult check

1.54   You should find that the tapping brought the fish to the surface for food.

1.55   All data will vary

1.56   Answers will be based on data from 1.55 Generally, there should be improvement of performance with more trials.

1.57   Each individual will be different

1.58   When the writing is natural by habit it goes fast because no thinking is necessary. When the writing is done by the unnatural hand, the number is decreased greatly because each action must be consciously thought out.

1.59   Answers will vary

1.60   Any order:

      a. conditional response

      b. trial and error

      c. habit

1.61   They were dogs trained by a Russian physiologist, Ivan P. Pavlov, in the early 1900s for an experiment which demonstrated conditional response.

1.62   "Trial and error" is a type of learning that takes place by trying many things in a variety of ways in order to produce the desired results. Examples might be working a puzzle, learning to ride a bike, learning to walk, or learning to eat.

1.63   Any order:

      a. simple motor act

      b. habits of adjustment

1.64   Teacher/Adult check. Answers will vary

1.65   a. X

      b. 3

      c. 2

      d. 4

      e. 1

      f. X

      g. 7

      h. 6

      i. 5

1.66   a. When I consider thy heavens, the work of thy fingers; the moon and the stars, which thou hast ordained;

      b. What is man, that thou art mindful of him? and the son of man, that thou visitest him?

c. For thou hast made him a little lower than the angels, and hast crowned him with glory and honor.

d. Thou madest him to have dominion over the works of thy hands; thou hast put all things under his feet:

e. All sheep and oxen, yea, and the beasts of the field;

f. the fowl of the air and the fish of the sea, and whatsoever passeth through the paths of the seas.

g. O Lord our Lord, how excellent is thy name in all the earth!

1.67 Man seems of little importance compared to the moon and the stars. David wonders how God can know and be interested in man.

1.68 Example: God has given man a high position. God has crowned man with glory and honor.

1.69 Man's position is just a little lower than that of the angels. (NOTE: The word translated angels is in Hebrew the word Elohim, which when directly translated means God. It is the same word used in Genesis 1.1.)

1.70 Man is given charge of all things.

1.71 Example: The Lord's name is excellent and in the highest position in all the earth. (Teacher/Adult check)

SECTION TWO

2.1 a. Should predict that the root will curl down and the stem will curl up.

b. The root will turn 90 degrees downward and the stem will curl 90 degrees upward.

c. The plants' roots will be pointing downward, and the stems and leaves will be more upward.

2.2 Drawing should be neat.

2.3 geotropism, hydrotropism and phototropism

2.4 The plant will bend and grow toward the hole.

2.5 phototropism

2.6 The root will bend and grow toward the wet soil at the right side of the container.

2.7 hydrotropism

2.8 The auxins concentrate on the wet side of the root and cause these cells to grow shorter than normal. This bends the root toward the water.

2.9 a. Answer should summarize the characteristics of the plant.

b. Answers should summarize the characteristics of the plant.

c. Answer should summarize the characteristics of the plant.

SECTION THREE

3.1 Any order:

a. tundra

b. northern coniferous forests or taiga

c. deciduous forests

d. tropical forests

e. grasslands

f. deserts

3.2 Teacher/Adult check

3.3 a. Answers depend upon biomes selected.

b. Compare answers directly with the text on biomes.

3.4 Teacher/Adult check

3.5 An ecological grouping of plants and animals, living in balance with one another.

3.6 a. marine biomes

   b. fresh water biomes

3.7 plankton

3.8 too dark

3.9 glowing lights

3.10 Any order:

   a. waves

   b. tides

3.11 suction cups

3.12 saltiness

3.13 Teacher/Adult check

3.14 a. consumer

   b. consumer

   c. consumer or decomposer

   d. consumer

   e. consumer

   f. consumer

   g. producer

   h. consumer or decomposer

3.15 grass-rabbit-fox-bacteria

3.16 Answers can vary

   a. grass

   b. trees

   c. rabbit

   d. cow

   e. ox

   f. snake

   g. eagle

   h. crow

   i. bacteria

   j. fungus

   k. man

   l. coyote

3.17 Organic fertilizers are the nutrients that fungi and bacteria produce from dead plants, animals, and people.

3.18 Example: Bacteria and fungi decompose the tissues of dead animals, plants, and humans and release minerals, carbon dioxide, and water for the plants to use.

3.19 The process of starting a series of steps, going through the steps, and ending up where one started is a cycle.

3.20 Any order:

   a. carbon-hydrogen-oxygen

   b. phosphorus or calcium

   c. nitrogen

3.21 May describe any one of the three studied. Look for good detail.

3.22 Plants and animals living together in a balance of species and population is a balance of nature.

3.23 The process by which organisms live in a very close relationship with one another.

3.24

Type	Meaning
a. commensalism	one organism helped but the other is not affected
b. mutualism	two organisms live together and both are helped
c. parasitism	parasite lives off the host; parasite helped, host harmed

3.25 Teacher/Adult check

SECTION ONE

1.1 usually football shaped

1.2 generally yellow—may vary

1.3 yes—generally

1.4 7

1.5 depends on flower

1.6 Teacher/Adult check

1.7 receptacle

1.8 depends on flower

1.9 depends on flower

1.10 depends on flower

1.11 a. yes

b. depends on flower, teacher check

1.12 mitosis

1.13 a. sperm

b. egg

1.14 nucleus

1.15 mitosis

1.16 genes

1.17 Example: Reduction division reduces the number of chromosomes in the egg and sperm cells. The sperm cells are carried in pollen to a flower that can be cross-pollinated. The pollen gets stuck in the sugary substance on the stigma and forms a tube to the ovary for the sperm cell to travel to the ovule.

1.18 yes…yes

1.19 Teacher/Adult check

1.20 Example: The egg cell is reduced to 1/2 chromosome number and the sperm is also reduced. When fertilization occurs, the chromosome number is restored.

1.21 7

1.22 It makes the pollen stick to the stigma.

1.23 mitosis

1.24 Self—when a plant receives pollen from within the flower.

Cross—receives pollen from another plant.

1.25 Cell division which results in new cells with the same number of chromosomes.

1.26 Cell division in which the chromosomes are reduced to half the original number.

1.27 reproductive cells only

SECTION TWO

2.1 3/4, 75%

2.2 1/4, 25%

2.3 1/4

2.4 1/2

2.5–2.9 Hint: Answer depends on peas selected. The purpose is to observe some traits that Mendel observed.

2.10 3/4

2.11 1/4

2.12 25% YY

2.13 25% yy

2.14 Hint: Various flavors can be tasted.

2.15 Depends on the individual's tastes.

2.16

	R	r
R	RR	Rr
r	Rr	rr

2.17 Teacher/Adult check

2.18 1/4

2.19 1/2

2.20 1/4

2.21 Teacher/Adult check

SECTION THREE

3.1   sugar (ribose)

3.2   giant

3.3   oxygen

3.4   sugar

3.5   alphabet

3.6   chlorophyll

3.7   Any of the following:
       white mice, white rabbits, white plants

3.8   DNA

3.9   lack of other color allows red blood vessels to show

3.10   all of the surroundings of a living organism

3.11   color

3.12   albino

3.13   genetics or heredity

3.14

	C	c
C	CC	Cc
c	Cc	cc

3.15   3/4

3.16   1/4

3.17   25

3.18   75

3.19   Teacher/Adult check

3.20–3.24   Teacher/Adult check

3.25   fact

3.26   not fact; mutations do not change the kinds

3.27   not fact; many result in death of the plant. Many plants were never edible.

3.28   fact

3.29   not fact; man doesn't make his own food with chlorophyll. Plants die because they can't make their own food.

3.30   not fact; they may have suffered a disease or nutritional deficiency.

3.31   not fact; some may be poisonous.

3.32   Example: Warm temperature causes the genes to produce white hair; cool temperatures cause black.

3.33   the genes for color

3.34   heredity and environment or temperature and environment

3.35   at the ends

3.36   in the center

3.37   Teacher/Adult check

3.38   no

3.39   Example: The environment (pea pod) has forced the peas to be small in the end of each pod. (Teacher/Adult check)

SECTION ONE

1.1   Examples:

a. desk

b. water in a vase

c. air

1.2   yes

1.3   yes

1.4   yes

1.5   It takes the shape of the container.

1.6   yes

1.7   a. gaseous

1.8   b. chemicals

1.9   c. mass

1.10 b. less than

1.11 c. the same as

1.12 a. has a fixed volume but takes the shape of its container

1.13 b. has the volume and shape of its container

1.14 c. has a fixed volume and shape

1.15 d

1.16 f

1.17 a

1.18 c

1.19 h

1.20 g

1.21 a. Planetary Model—attempts to show that electrons "orbit" around the nucleus like planets do around the sun.

b. Electron Cloud Model—shows that electrons swarm about the nucleus in an incredibly fast way.

c. Simplified Model—attempts to simplify electron positions as they move around the nucleus. It is easier to draw than the electron cloud model.

1.22 Teacher/Adult check: Drawing should show one electron outside the nucleus of the atom, and should be properly labeled.

1.23 atom

1.24 matter

1.25 molecules

1.26 compound

1.27 oxygen

1.28 Carbon dioxide

1.29 salt or table salt

1.30 copper iodide

1.31 1. solid, yes, yes

2. liquid, yes, no

3. gas, no, no

1.32 An atom is the smallest particle of an element.

1.33 A molecule is the chemical combination of two or more atoms.

1.34 An element is a pure substance that cannot be broken down chemically into simpler substances.

1.35 A compound is a substance whose molecules consist of atoms which are chemically combined.

1.36 calcium carbonate

1.37 a. no

b. yes

c. no

d. yes

SECTION TWO

2.1   20

2.2   2

2.3   Au

2.4   Fe

2.5   K

2.6 H_2O

2.7 CO_2

2.8   2

2.9   carbon

2.10   plus (+) or positive

2.11   neutral

2.12   minus (-) or negative

2.13   protons + neutrons

2.14   hydrogen

2.15   a. Ca
       b. C
       c. Cl
       d. Co
       e. Cu
       f. F
       g. Au
       h. He
       i. H
       j. I
       k. Fe
       l. Pb
       m. Mg
       n. Ni
       o. N
       p. O
       q. P
       r. K
       s. Si
       t. Ag
       u. Na
       v. S
       w. Sn
       x. U
       y. Zn

2.16   a. protons
       b. neutrons
       c. electrons

2.17   Teacher/Adult check

2.18   metals

2.19   Hydrogen is an exception to the rule.

2.20   nonmetals

2.21   rare earth

2.22   man-made elements

2.23   19

2.24   36

2.25   periods

2.26   group

2.27   radioactive elements

2.28–2.31   Teacher/Adult check

2.32   a. calcium
       b. carbon
       c. chlorine
       d. cobalt
       e. copper
       f. fluorine
       g. gold
       h. helium
       i. hydrogen
       j. iodine
       k. iron
       l. lead
       m. magnesium
       n. nickel

o. nitrogen

p. oxygen

q. phosphorus

r. potassium

s. silicon

t. silver

u. sodium

v. sulfur

w. tin

x. uranium

y. zinc

2.33 Examples:

a. fluorine in water; iron in steel parts of desks

b. copper in telephone wire; gold in jewelry

c. oxygen in air and water; hydrogen in water

d. carbon in air; tin in box or can

e. calcium in bones; iron and potassium in bodies

SECTION THREE

3.1 Teacher/Adult check. Diagram must show 11 protons and 12 neutrons in the nucleus, with 2 electrons in the K shell, 8 electrons in the L shell, and 1 electron in the M shell.

3.2 18

3.3 17

3.4 Teacher/Adult check. Diagram must show 17 protons and 18 neutrons in the nucleus, with 2 electrons in the K shell, 8 electrons in the L shell, and 7 electrons in the M shell.

3.5 helium, 2

lithium, 4

3.6 a. See previous diagram requirements for helium

b. See previous diagram requirements for lithium

3.7 a. atomic number (no. of protons)

b. chemical symbol (nitrogen)

c. atomic weight (protons and neutrons)

3.8 8

3.9 a positively charged nucleus, with negatively charged electrons whirling around the nucleus.

3.10 Teacher/Adult check

3.11 Niels Bohr

3.12 could only travel in certain successively larger orbits around the nucleus.

3.13 more electrons

3.14 phenolphthalein

3.15 ammonia, baking soda

3.16 boric acid, citric acid, or acetic

3.17 $NaCl$, H_2O, CO_2

3.18 citric

3.19   acetic

3.20   neutralized

3.21   indicators

3.22   a. acid
       b. base
       c. base
       d. base
       e. acid

3.23   phenolphthalein

3.24   red

3.25   Either order:
       a. slick
       b. soapy

3.26   An indicator is a substance which changes color in the presence of an acid or base.

3.27   An acid is a substance which tastes sour or sharp.

3.28   a. freezing (temperature)
       b. it floats

3.29   a. heat
       b. bending

3.30   a. heat
       b. It occupies more space.

3.31   Example: The river overflowed its bank because of unusually heavy rainstorms. The effect of the high-rising river is flooding.

3.32   Example: Add an acid to a base and it will neutralize. The acid causes the base to neutralize. The effect is neutralization; or you could say the effect results in neither substance being an acid or a base (they are neutral).

3.33   Teacher/Adult check

SECTION ONE

1.1   b. vibration

1.2   a. waves

1.3   b. larynx

1.4   c. tightened vocal chords

1.5   c. vibrations

1.6   Sound waves start vibrations on the sensitive part of your ear. As the sound waves reach the eardrum located within the ear, the eardrum begins to vibrate in the same way as the object that originally produced the sound. The vibrating eardrum, in turn, causes the bones of the middle ear to vibrate. These vibrations are transferred to the nerves in the inner ear. The nerves carry the messages to the brain, enabling us to interpret the sounds that we hear.

1.7   The tube with the longest column of air has the lowest sound.

1.8   The tube with the shortest column of air has the highest sound.

1.9   The one with the longest column of air has the lowest notes.

1.10 Teacher/Adult check

1.11 The vibrations cause the water to splash.

1.12 yes

1.13 medium

1.14 a. density

b. compressibility

c. medium

1.15 1,100 feet per second

1.16 compression, rarefaction

1.17 pitch

1.18 amplitude

1.19 loudness

1.20 Noise

1.21 less air molecules

1.22 a. No

b. There is no medium that can transmit the sound waves.

1.23 Teacher/Adult check

1.24 crest

1.25 trough

1.26 Yes, a wavelength is from crest to crest. Teacher/Adult check

1.27 g

1.28 i

1.29 b

1.30 a

1.31 e

1.32 c

1.33 h

1.34 f

1.35 It appears to move closer as water is added.

1.36 The light is bent (refracted) making the coin appear to be closer.

1.37 It appears bent.

1.38 It appears to be in two pieces.

1.39 The changed appearance is due to the refraction of light.

1.40 true

1.41 true

1.42 true

1.43 false

1.44 true

1.45 false

1.46 false

1.47 true

1.48 false

SECTION TWO

2.1 Sir Isaac Newton

2.2 darkening a room, putting a slit in the shutter, and putting a prism where the beam of light came in

2.3 spectrum

2.4 a. red
b. orange
c. yellow
d. green
e. blue
f. indigo
g. violet

2.5 red

2.6 violet

2.7 triangular in shape

2.8 red

2.9 violet

2.10 prism

2.11 refract

2.12 a. red
b. orange
c. yellow
d. green
e. blue
f. indigo
g. violet

2.13 When light rays reach a prism, they are bent differently because they are of different wavelengths. As the light waves are bent, different colors are formed. They cannot go back together because the prism is triangular.

2.14 violet

2.15 red

2.16 student check

2.17 Red, orange, yellow, green, blue, indigo, and violet are the colors.

2.18 The water in the glass was used to separate the colors.

2.19 red

2.20 violet

2.21 red light

2.22 violet light

SECTION THREE

3.1 reflect light

3.2 all colors

3.3 to throw back to your eye

3.4 spectrum

3.5 absorbed

3.6 green

3.7 The green color is reflected to the eye.

3.8 black

3.9 Black absorbs most colors.

3.10 The green cellophane enhanced the green color of the paper.

3.11 Double-filtered green is reflected to the eye.

3.12 Neutral dark gray or black

3.13 Green is at the middle of the color spectrum and absorbs the red color and does not allow it to pass through.

3.14 The black appears even darker because all the reflection of light has been blocked.

3.15 Because the colors appear white as the color wheel is spun, we can see that white is a mixture of all colors.

3.16 yellow

3.17 violet

3.18 blue-green

3.19 Any order:
   a. red
   b. green
   c. blue

3.20 white

3.21 colorants

3.22 yellow

3.23 Either order:
   a. blue
   b. red

3.24 green

3.25 black

3.26 dark gray or black

3.27 green

3.28 to take up

3.29 to throw back to your eye

3.30 white

3.31 add

3.32 subtract

3.33 green

3.34 orange

3.35 violet (purple)

3.36 black

3.37 no

3.38 a. red
   b. yellow
   c. blue

3.39 colorants

3.40 dyes

3.41 pigments

3.42 orange

3.43 green

3.44 violet (purple)

3.45 a. orange
   b. green
   c. violet

3.46 black

3.47 reflects

3.48 a. red
   b. green
   c. blue

3.49 add to

3.50 subtract from

SECTION ONE

1.1 Motion occurs when an object moves through space.

1.2 Force is any cause that changes the motion or shape of an object.

1.3 Work is the amount of force on an object times the distance the object moves.

1.4 Any order:

   a. muscular force, man pushing piano

   b. wind force, windmill

   c. water force, water moves turbine

1.5 g

1.6 f

1.7 c

1.8 b

1.9 e

1.10 h

1.11 a

1.12 d

1.13 a. 100 foot-pounds

   b. 200 foot-pounds

   c. 370 foot-pounds

   d. 2900 foot-pounds

   e. 2 newton-meters

   f. 60 kilogram-meters

1.14 Adult check

1.15 Adult check

1.16 Adult check

1.17 Adult check

1.18 Adult check

1.19 It requires more force to lift an object than to pull it because you must lift it against the pull of gravity.

1.20 Adult check

1.21 a. force

   b. work

   c. gravity

   d. foot-pound

   e. kilogram-meter

SECTION TWO

2.1 Power, in the scientific sense, is the speed or rate of doing work.

2.2 Two boys run 100 yards. One does it in 11 seconds, the other in 12 seconds. Both did the same work at different speeds.

2.3 a. "For I am not ashamed of the gospel of Christ: for it is the power of God unto salvation to every one that believeth; to the Jew first, and also to the Greek."

   b. The meaning of power as it is used in this Scripture is God's divine ability or authority to bring about change.

2.4 Adult check

2.5 Adult check

2.6 550 x 100 = 55,000

2.7 No. A car might have high horsepower and be a very poor car otherwise. The total horsepower of a car is rarely needed for good performance. If a car has 120 HP, does that mean that the car is not as good as the one with 200HP? The car with the higher power may use more gasoline.

2.8 Adult check

2.9 Adult check

2.10 Horsepower is the unit for measuring the power of engines and motors.

2.11 746

2.12 The washer with 482 watts has the greater power because one-half of 746 watts is 373.

2.13 a. 1440
b. 1092
c. James

2.14 James Watt

2.15 Answer may vary but should mirror concepts taught in the LIFEPAC. The 80-pound object moved ten feet would be 800 foot-pounds of work being done because 80 x 10 = 800 foot-pounds. The 160-pound object being moved five feet would also be 800 foot-pounds of work because 160 x 5 = 800 foot-pounds of work being done.

2.16 110 x 550 = 60,500

2.17 A Summary of the Second Law

1. Sir Isaac Newton's Second Law of Motion: the rate of change of movement in a straight line is proportional to the size of the force and takes place in the same direction that the force is applied.

2. Magnitude is defined as the *size of the force applied.* Mass is defined as *the amount of matter: in an object, or a measure of the inertia in an object.* Acceleration is defined as *the increase of velocity, or the distance traveled in one direction.*

3. Force, mass, and acceleration are related by Newton's second law of motion by the equation F = ma, where F = Force, m = mass, and a = acceleration. The change that a force makes in the motion of an object depends on the magnitude of the force and the mass of the object. The greater the force, the greater the acceleration; the greater the mass, the smaller the acceleration.

4. Examples: If two balls of the same size but different masses are kicked with the same force, the lighter ball will travel more distance in the time period than the heavier ball. A baseball hit by a professional baseball player will travel with greater acceleration than the same ball hit by a sixth-grader, because the force of the professional player is greater than that of the sixth-grader.

A summary of the Third Law

1. Sir Isaac Newton's Third Law of Motion: for every action there is an equal and opposite reaction.

2. no terms to define

3. An action always has a result. These results are always equal in magnitude to the action, but occur in the opposite direction.

4. Examples: When a garden hose with water spraying through a nozzle is left lying on the ground, it will move backwards, or in the opposite direction of the spraying water. When you fire a rifle there is a kick or recoil. The explosion of the gunpowder occurs in all directions, causing the bullet to escape through the barrel of the rifle, while the rifle itself pushes back against your shoulder in the opposite direction. The hanging ball puzzle also demonstrates this law. Six metal balls are touching each other in a single line and hanging by a string. If you pull two balls from one end of the line and allow them to strike the others, two balls will fly outward from the other end. Similarly, if four balls are allowed to strike the line, four will move outwardly from the opposite end.

A summary of the Law of Gravitation

1. Sir Isaac Newton's Law of Gravitation: the force of attraction between two objects is related directly to the size of their masses.

2. Gravity (gravitation) is defined as the *force that pulls things toward the center of the earth and which accounts for the fact that all matter is attracted to other bits of matter in the universe.* Gravitational Force is defined as the *natural attraction between massive bodies that influences all interactions of matter.* Mass is defined as the *amount of matter in an object, or a measure of the inertia in an object.*

3. All objects in the universe attract one another, and this attraction is related to the size of their masses. The larger either object's mass is, the stronger the attraction (greater the force) between the two objects. The gravitational force, or "attraction" is oppositely proportional to the distance between the centers of gravity of the two objects squared (multiplied by itself). For example, as the distance between the two objects is doubled, the force between them decreases by one-fourth the original strength.

4. Examples: An object's weight (the strength of the gravitational force pulling on it) is not the same on the earth as on the moon. The gravitational force of the moon on the object is less (it has less mass) compared to the earth; therefore, the object will weigh less on the moon. An object would weigh nothing at the center of the earth because the earth pulls on it equally from all directions.

2.18 Objects at rest tend to remain at rest unless acted upon by some outside force.

2.19 Example: All masses in the universe attract one another.

2.20 Rate of change of movement in a straight line is proportional to the size of the force and is in the same direction that the force is applied.

2.21 For every action there is an equal and opposite reaction.

SECTION THREE

3.1 A machine is a mechanical device people use to help them do work. Example: A bicycle is a machine to help me move.

3.2 Examples:
   a. Pencils writing on paper
   b. Sliding a box up a ramp
   c. Metal rubbing against metal in a nut and bolt (screw)
   d. Broom rubbing against floor (lever)
   e. Rope going over a wheel (pulley)
   f. Shovel digging gravel

3.3 inertia or lack of friction

3.4 gravity

3.5 friction

3.6 lack of friction

3.7 friction

3.8 inertia or lack of friction

3.9 friction

3.10 inertia

3.11 lack of friction, inertia, or gravity

3.12 that an object at rest tends to remain at rest or to continue in motion in a straight line with constant speed unless acted upon by some outside force.

3.13 *Work in* equals *work out.*

3.14   Example; either order:
    a. windmill
    b. water wheel

3.15   electricity

3.16   Examples: windmill, water wheel,
       water turbine

SECTION ONE

1.1 a. 7,900 miles

b. 7,926 miles

c. 26 miles

d. no

1.2 true

1.3 false

1.4 true

1.5 true

1.6 true

1.7 false

1.8 false

1.9 true

1.10 The rotation of the earth about its axis causes night and day.

1.11 In relation to the sun, the earth takes 24 hours to make one complete rotation about its axis. This is called a *solar day*. In relation to the very same position on earth compared to far distant stars, however, the earth takes 23 hours 56 minutes 4.091 seconds to make one complete rotation. This is called a *sidereal day*.

1.12 The distance around the earth parallel to the equator varies, depending on where you are located. At the equator, the distance around the earth is the greatest. As you move toward either pole, the distance is smaller. Therefore, you travel less in a day as you move toward the poles from the equator, and the speed of motion would be less.

1.13 a. sunset

1.14 c. midnight

1.15 d. 1800

1.16 d. 360

1.17 b. Standard time

1.18 b. Prime Meridian

1.19 a. International Date Line

1.20 b. four

1.21 f

1.22 h

1.23 g

1.24 a

1.25 j

1.26 b

1.27 k

1.28 c

1.29 l

1.30 d

1.31 The day and night are an equal amount of time. Also, the sun is directly overhead at noon on the equator.

1.32 In the Northern hemisphere, after the vernal equinox, the days become longer. After the autumnal equinox, the days become shorter.

1.33 No. Scientific study is limited by the facts that mankind has observed on the earth, in the lab, and in his explorations with a microscope or telescope. Mankind can only imagine what conditions exist on a planet orbiting a star in a faraway solar system or galaxy.

1.34 Adult check

SECTION TWO

2.1 There is less of the tree visible, until it is eventually blocked from sight.

2.2 a. moon

Either order:

b. earth

c. sun

2.3 a. two

b. three

2.4 They have been able to determine the exact relative positions of the earth, sun, and moon. They have been able to study possible changes in the strength of gravity and the size of the sun. The size of distant stars has been determined through the study of eclipses of other heavenly bodies.

2.5 true

2.6 false

2.7 true

2.8 true

2.9 false

2.10 true

2.11 false

2.12 b

2.13 a

2.14 c

2.15 b

2.16 c

2.17 a

2.18 the earth, moon, and sun are nearly in a straight line and the moon passes between the earth and sun.

2.19 a total or partial obscuring (or darkening) of one celestial body by another.

2.20 the earth, moon, and sun are nearly in a straight line and the moon passes through the earth's shadow.

2.21 pertaining to the moon.

2.22 pertaining to the sun.

2.23 During a solar eclipse, the line-up is sun, moon, and earth. During a lunar eclipse, the line-up is sun, earth, and moon.

2.24 a. opinion

b. fact

c. fact

d. fact

e. opinion

f. opinion

g. opinion

h. fact

i. opinion

j. fact

k. fact

l. fact

2.25 a. syl lab i ca tion

b. rev o lu tion

c. sat el lite

d. ro ta tion

e. ev o lu tion

f. hor i zon tal ly

g. ver ti cal ly

h. el lip ti cal ly

i. grav i ta tion

j. in er tia

SECTION THREE

3.1–3.3 Answers may vary. The answers given are close approximations.

3.1 109

3.2 863,934

3.3 a. 863,934
     b. 865,000

3.4 star

3.5 99

3.6 Either order:
     a. hydrogen
     b. helium

3.7 nuclear fusion

3.8 10,000° F

3.9 solar activity

3.10 cooler

3.11 prominences

3.12 Solar flares

3.13 northern and southern lights

3.14 true

3.15 false

3.16 true

3.17 true

3.18 true

3.19 Teacher/Adult check

3.20 Adult check

3.21 a. Mercury
      b. Venus
      c. Earth
      d. Mars
      e. Jupiter
      f. Saturn
      g. Uranus
      h. Neptune

3.22 h

3.23 i

3.24 f

3.25 g

3.26 a

3.27 e

3.28 b

3.19

Planets	Diameter (miles)	Distance from the sun (mean)	Number of Moons	Day (hrs)	Year (yrs)
Mercury	3,031	36,000,000	0	1,416	.24
Venus	7,520	67,250,000	0	5,832	.6
Earth	7,926	93,000,000	1	24	1
Mars	4,200	141,700,000	2	24.5	1.8
Jupiter	88,700	483,700,000	16	10	12
Saturn	74,600	885,200,000	23	10.5	29.5
Uranus	31,570	1,781,000,000	15	17	84
Neptune*	30,200	2,788,000,000	2	16*	165

*Reports from Voyager 2 state the spin on its axis is 16 to 28 hrs.; they are not sure, but it's within that range.

SECTION ONE

1.1 true

1.2 false

1.3 true

1.4 true

1.5 false

1.6 true

1.7 false

1.8 false

1.9 i

1.10 j

1.11 m

1.12 l

1.13 k

1.14 b

1.15 a

1.16 c

1.17 n

1.18 h

1.19 e

1.20 g

1.21 adult check

1.22 space travel

1.23 Hubble Space Telescope (HST)

1.24 Chandra X-ray Observatory

1.25 Very Large Array (VLA)

1.26 amateur astronomers

1.27 adult check

SECTION TWO

2.1 adult check

2.2 Possibly 2 or 3 red stars; depends on location, time of year, and weather. Adult check.

2.3 b

2.4 c

2.5 b

2.6 c

2.7 b

2.8 The color of a star tells approximately how hot it is. Stars range from red to blue-white in color and surface temperatures from 5,500 to 55,000 degrees Fahrenheit. Our sun is a medium yellow star with a surface temperature of about 10,000 degrees Fahrenheit.

2.9 supergiant reds

2.10 white dwarfs

2.11 medium

2.12 865,000

2.13 Betelgeuse

2.14 companion

2.15 Rigel

2.16 the sun

2.17 continuous

2.18 bright-line

2.19 bright-line

2.20 c

2.21 c

2.22 a

2.23 b

2.24 b

2.25 the colors of the spectrum

2.26 the same

2.27 continuous

2.28 This order:

   a. red
   b. orange
   c. yellow
   d. green
   e. blue
   f. indigo
   g. violet

2.29 Any order:
   a. continuous
   b. dark-line
   c. bright-line

2.30 Answer may vary.

   Example: Astronomers have discovered the continuous spectrum, brightline spectrum, and the darkline spectrum. With the spectroscope, scientists are able to tell what a star is made of. Helium, one of the gases that the sun is composed of, was discovered in the spectrum of the sun before it was discovered on earth.

2.31 tells how bright a star appears to an observer on earth

2.32 the true or real brightness of a star

2.33 Betelgeuse

2.34 Betelgeuse

2.35 f

2.36 c

2.37 d

2.38 e

2.39 b

2.40 g

2.41 a

SECTION THREE

3.1 constellation

3.2 88

3.3 1,000 – 1,500

3.4 northern

3.5 Orion, Pleiades

3.6 southernmost

3.7 latitudes

3.8 false

3.9 true

3.10 false

3.11 true

3.12 false

3.13 true

3.14 false

3.15 false

3.16 Example:
   a. The man wore a mizar.
   b. Mizar is located in the Big Dipper

3.17 Example:
   a. Mercury is a liquid metal used in thermometers.
   b. Mercury is the smallest planet in our solar system.

3.18 Example:
   a. An artificial satellite was launched in June.
   b. Our moon is a natural satellite.

3.19 Example:
   a. Sodium chloride is a binary compound.
   b. Mizar is a binary star system.

3.20 Example:
   a. The story was about Jupiter.
   b. Jupiter is the largest planet.

3.21 a. He telleth the number of the stars; he calleth them all by their names.
   b. Thou art worthy, O Lord, to receive glory and honour and power: for thou hast created all things, and for thy pleasure they are and were created.
   c. Amos 5:8: Seek him that maketh the seven stars and Orion, and turneth the shadow of death into the morning, and maketh the day dark with night: that calleth for the waters of the sea, and poureth them out upon the face of the earth: The LORD is his name:

3.22 c

3.23 d

3.24 a

3.25 b

3.26 b

3.27 b

3.28 a

3.29 Adult check

3.30 Adult check. Example: Every place on earth can be measured by latitude lines and be able to see the same things–but from a different angle.

SECTION ONE

1.1   leaf

1.2   chlorophyll

1.3   glucose

1.4   starch

1.5   oxygen

1.6   sun

1.7   Any order:
    a. fats
    b. oils
    c. proteins
    d. vitamins

1.8   e

1.9   d

1.10 c

1.11 a

1.12 b

1.13 starch

1.14 Any order:
    a. fats
    b. oils
    c. proteins
    d. vitamins

1.15 Any order:
    a. root
    b. stem
    c. leaves

1.16 e

1.17 d

1.18 f

1.19 b

1.20 a

1.21 true

1.22 true

1.23 true

1.24 false

1.25 true

1.26 true

1.27 adult check

1.28 positive

1.29 negative

1.30 water

1.31 earth

1.32 light

1.33 a. mouth
    b. esophagus
    c. stomach
    d. small intestine
    e. large intestine
    f. rectum

1.34 The parts of the body through which food passes

1.35 It churns the food and adds digestive juices

1.36 b. absorb water

1.37 a. absorb food

1.38 d. make an emulsion of fats

1.39 c. producing enzymes

1.40 c. liver

1.41 skin

1.42 carbon dioxide

1.43 oxygen

1.44 kidneys

1.45 villi

1.46 skin

1.47 a. arteries
      b. veins

1.48 capillaries

1.49 d

1.50 b

1.51 b

1.52 a

1.53 a

1.54 c

1.55 b

1.56 d

1.57 f

1.58 d

1.59 c

1.60 b

1.61 a

1.62 e

1.63 1/4

1.64 d

1.65 j

1.66 h

1.67 c

1.68 i

1.69 e

1.70 b

1.71 f

1.72 a

1.73 Examples:

a. The tundra is a treeless, northern area, frozen most of the time. Plant life includes lichens, mosses, and a few flowering plants. Animal life includes polar bears, snowshoe hares, caribou, and birds.

b. The northern coniferous forest contains conifers. It contains animal life such as moose, black bears, wolves, rodents, and birds.

c. This area contains trees that shed their leaves during the winter. It includes mostly maple, oak, elm, beech, and birch trees. Animals include the deer, puma, squirrels, birds, and foxes.

d. Grasslands are plains and prairies. They are characterized by an abundance of cereals and grasses. The animal life is mostly small rodents.

e. A tropical rain forest is found where the climate is hot and humid. It has abundant life; both plants and animals abound.

f. A desert biome is characterized by dryness. Fewer animals can survive. Cacti or similar plants are about all that can survive.

1.74 legumes, such as beans, peas, and soybeans or alfalfa

1.75 bacteria and fungi

1.76 plants

1.77 plants

SECTION TWO

2.1   a

2.2   d

2.3   b

2.4   g

2.5   h

2.6   e

2.7   f

2.8   a. K
      b. Na
      c. Sn
      d. Fe
      e. Zn
      f. F
      g. He
      h. C
      i. Cl
      j. Ca
      k. H
      l. S
      m. Ag
      n. Au

2.9   a. copper
      b. magnesium
      c. nitrogen
      d. phosphorus
      e. uranium
      f. silicon
      g. nickel
      h. cobalt
      i. lead
      j. oxygen
      k. calcium
      l. potassium

2.10   adult check

2.11   a. violet
       b. indigo
       c. blue
       d. green
       e. yellow
       f. orange
       g. red

2.12   Any order:
       a. red
       b. green
       c. blue

2.13   white

2.14   yellow

2.15   red

2.16   a. 186,000
       b. second

2.17   Any order:
       a. red
       b. yellow
       c. blue

2.18   a. orange
       b. green
       c. violet

2.19   a. transparent
       b. translucent
       c. opaque

2.20   Examples: mat, pat, trim, electric, sect, rum, train, pain, rat, cat, spat, game, select

2.21   d

2.22   i

2.23	a
2.24	g
2.25	f
2.26	h
2.27	c
2.28	e

2.29 700 foot-pounds

2.30 14 kilogram-meters

2.31 the rate or speed of doing work

2.32 The work output of a machine equals the work put into the machine.

2.33 Friction is a force that opposes work. It is a hindrance because parts move against one another.

2.34 The highway is slippery. You need friction for your tires to stop.

SECTION THREE

3.1	h
3.2	g
3.3	e
3.4	b
3.5	i
3.6	c
3.7	f
3.8	a
3.9	d
3.10	l

3.11 365 $\frac{1}{4}$ days or 365

3.12 curving pathway in space.

3.13 Either order:

a. the tilt of the earth

b. orbit of the earth around the sun

3.14 a June 21

b. December 22

3.15 The equinox is the time when days and nights are equal.

3.16 Solar eclipse

sun - moon - earth

During a solar eclipse, the sun is darkened because the moon is between the earth and the sun.

3.17 Lunar eclipse

sun - earth - moon

During a lunar eclipse, the moon is darkened because the earth casts a shadow in it.

444

444444444444

3.18 j

3.19 a

3.20 d

3.21 c

3.22 h

3.23 f

3.24 e

3.25 i

3.26 b

3.27 reflected

3.28 Mercury

3.29 Jupiter

3.30 Any order:
   a. oxygen
   b. water
   c. climate

3.31 planet

3.32 groups of particles consisting of rocks, metals, and frozen gases

3.33 meteor

3.34 meteor that hits the earth

3.35 Venus

3.36 f

3.37 g

3.38 h

3.39 i

3.40 b

3.41 j

3.42 c

3.43 a

3.44 e

3.45 d

3.46 Any order:
   a. size
   b. color
   c. temperature
   d. brightness or magnitude

3.47 magnitude

3.48 medium

3.49 lines in the spectrum indicating elements are present

3.50 on the sun

3.51 its elements

3.52 giant blues

3.53 dwarf reds

3.54 A star is very bright, but from far away, it appears dim.

SELF TEST 1

1.01 h

1.02 g

1.03 a

1.04 l

1.05 c

1.06 k

1.07 m

1.08 e

1.09 f

1.010 i

1.011 red

1.012 glucose

1.013 oxygen

1.014 organic

1.015 Any order:
a. light (color)
b. water
c. minerals
d. carbon dioxide

1.016 Any order:
a. palisade
b. spongy

1.017 b

1.018 c

1.019 d

1.020 b

1.021 d

1.022 a

1.023 b

1.024 a

1.025 c

1.026 d

1.027 The leaf factory takes water and carbon dioxide with chlorophyll and light energy to make starch and oxygen.

1.028 Hint: This is a good place to receive oral answers and discussion.

1.029 Refer to diagram in LIFEPAC.

1.030 Example: I would give the plants the best fertilizer for their growth. I would put them in red light, keep them watered, and obtain a high carbon dioxide level.

SELF TEST 2

2.01	true		2.021	a
2.02	false		2.022	c
2.03	false		2.023	d
2.04	true		2.024	b
2.05	true		2.025	e
2.06	true		2.026	d
2.07	true		2.027	b
2.08	false		2.028	e
2.09	false		2.029	a
2.010	true		2.030	f
			2.031	c
2.011	b		2.032	g
2.012	c			
2.013	a		2.033	stem
2.014	c		2.034	starch or glucose
2.015	d		2.035	starch
2.016	a		2.036	cortex
2.017	a		2.037	starch
2.018	d		2.038	bark
2.019	a		2.039	oxygen
2.020	c		2.040	stem

SELF TEST 3

3.01   h

3.02   g

3.03   j

3.04   d

3.05   l

3.06   i

3.07   e

3.08   c

3.09   a

3.010   b

3.011   false

3.012   false

3.013   true

3.014   true

3.015   false

3.016   false

3.017   true

3.018   true

3.019   false

3.020   false

3.021   b

3.022   c

3.023   a

3.024   d

3.025   Any order:
a. anchor plants
b. transport water and minerals
c. store food

3.026   broad

3.027   tissue decay

3.028   cortex

3.029   glucose

3.030   The grass will turn yellow because it can't get sunlight and the chloroplasts die.

3.031   Plant veins transport minerals and water from the roots to the leaf tips.

3.032   The stomata open and close, letting oxygen out and carbon dioxide into the leaf.

3.033   When the leaf dies, the chloroplast dies. This causes the green chlorophyll to be lost so the other colors can be seen.

SELF TEST 1

1.01   e

1.02   a

1.03   c

1.04   b

1.05   f

1.06   d

1.07   c

1.08   a

1.09   e

1.010   b

1.011   Either order:

  a. to grind food

  b. to add saliva

1.012   a. mouth

  b. stomach

1.013   Either order:

  a. digestion

  b. grinding

1.014   Either order:

  a. food digestion (fats especially)

  b. absorbing dissolved food into the blood stream

1.015   Either order:

  a. remove water to be used again

  b. collect undissolved food and harmful wastes

1.016   b

1.017   c

1.018   d

1.019   a

1.020   b

1.021   d

1.022   b

1.023   c

1.024   b

1.025   b

1.026   a

1.027   b

1.028   c

1.029   d

1.030   e

1.031   h

1.032   f

1.033   g

1.034   b

1.035   a

1.036   The primary function of digestion is to break the food containing large, complex chemicals into small ones so the body can use the vitamins and minerals in the food. Answers may vary.

1.037   Examples, any order:

  a balanced diet, good hygiene, exercise, cleanliness

SELF TEST 2

2.01   f

2.02   d

2.03   h

2.04   c

2.05   b

2.06   j

2.07   e

2.08   i

2.09   g

2.010   a

2.011   Any order:

a. protection

b. cooling

c. removal of body wastes

d. sensing outside things with nerve cells

2.012   a. arteries

b. capillaries

c. veins

2.013   a. red cells

b. white cells

c. platelets

2.014   a. large vein from upper and lower halves of the body

b. right atrium

c. right ventricle

d. through valve to artery

e. artery to lungs

f. veins from lungs

g. left atrium

h. left ventricle

i. through valve

j. aorta

2.015   b

2.016   c

2.017   d

2.018   d

2.019   c

2.020   Partially digested food comes into the stomach. Enzymes, gastric juices, and mucus are added to digest starch and proteins. The churning action of the stomach further aids digestion.

2.021   The blood travels through the kidneys. The kidney filters out the waste liquid, purifies the blood of poisons and unused chemicals, and passes the urine produced on to the bladder.

2.022   Blood circulation—carries gases (oxygen and carbon dioxide) to purify the blood; skin—cools, excretes waste, protects and senses; kidney—purifies the blood of waste liquids; lungs—exchange oxygen for carbon dioxide in the blood

2.023   Any diseases relating to heart, lungs, skin, and kidney

SELF TEST 3

3.01 h

3.02 i

3.03 g

3.04 a

3.05 j

3.06 c

3.07 b

3.08 d

3.09 f

3.010 e

3.011 a. cranium
b. clavicle (collarbone)
c. sternum
d. radius
e. ulna
f. phalanges
g. patella (kneecap)
h. metatarsals
i. phalanges
j. tarsals
k. tibia
l. fibula
m. femur
n. carpals (wrist bones)
o. ilium (hip bone)
p. vertebrae
q. humerus
r. scapula (shoulder blade)

3.012 a. trapezius
b. chest muscle
c. abdominal muscle
d. gastrocnemius
e. thigh muscle

f. sartorius
g. biceps
h. triceps
i. deltoid

3.013 c

3.014 d

3.015 a

3.016 a

3.017 c

3.018 d

3.019 b

3.020 d

3.021 d

3.022 d

3.023 Any order:
a. cooling
b. protection
c. loss of wastes
d. sensing through nerve cells

3.024 Examples; any two, any order:
a. anemia
b. low iron in diet
c. leukemia
d. unknown
e. high blood pressure
f. smoking, tension, lack of exercise

3.025 Any order:
a. cancer
b. none known
c. muscular dystrophy
d. none known
e. rickets
f. high vitamin D diet and sunshine

SELF TEST 1

1.01	true
1.02	true
1.03	true
1.04	true
1.05	false
1.06	true
1.07	true
1.08	false
1.09	true
1.010	false
1.011	d
1.012	e
1.013	g
1.014	a
1.015	b
1.016	f
1.017	c
1.018	k
1.019	i
1.020	l

1.021 a. cerebrum
b. cerebellum
c. brain stem
d. frontal lobe
e. temporal lobe
f. parietal lobe
g. occipital lobe
h. left cerebral hemisphere
i. right cerebral hemisphere
j. longitudinal fissure

1.022 a. breathing, digestion, heartbeat

1.023 c. ganglia

1.024 a. slow down

1.025 a. survival mechanisms

1.026 c. sense organs

1.027 Any order:
a. cell body
b. axon
c. dendrites

1.028 Any order:
a. axon
b. dendrites

1.029 Answers may vary. Example: A dog learns to bark when a person says "speak" because he is rewarded for exhibiting the proper response. In essence, when one thing happens, we expect something else to happen as a result.

1.030 Teacher/Adult check. Remember to check the meaning against what the text has explained. Example: Man has written and spoken languages. Humans can create music. Mankind has developed machines that can help him do work. Man can put the environment to work for him.

SELF TEST 2

2.01	h
2.02	f
2.03	b
2.04	b
2.05	j
2.06	j
2.07	i
2.08	a
2.09	d
2.010	g
2.011	b
2.012	c
2.013	d
2.014	a
2.015	e
2.016	b
2.017	d
2.018	a
2.019	c
2.020	b
2.021	false
2.022	true
2.023	false
2.024	false
2.025	true
2.026	false
2.027	true
2.028	true
2.029	false
2.030	true

2.031 Any order:

a. The leaflets will fold up along the stem if touched.

b. The slender stems supporting the leaflets will droop down if the touch is strong enough.

c. A little moisture is released into the atmosphere.

2.032 Any order:

a. It carries nerve messages from various body parts to the brain.

b. It intercepts and interprets danger signals from various parts of the body.

2.033 This tropism is due to the earth's pull (gravity) and causes roots to grow toward the soil and stems and leaves to grow away from the earth.

2.034 This tropism causes plant roots to grow toward (seek out) water.

2.035 This tropism causes plant stems and leaves to grow toward light.

2.036 A chemical produced in growing tips of roots, stems, and leaves. This chemical causes all growth to speed up or slow down. It is a regulatory chemical.

2.037 The brain controls and processes all body functions.

2.038 The chemical regulator called an auxin concentrates (collects) in one portion of a plant and speeds up or slows down cell growth to cause that portion of a plant to bend (usually on one side or the other of a stem, root, or leaf).

SELF TEST 3

3.01   a

3.02   l

3.03   g

3.04   j

3.05   k

3.06   b

3.07   o

3.08   d

3.09   e

3.010   c

3.011   m

3.012   n

3.013   h

3.014   f

3.015   i

3.016   a

3.017   b

3.018   d

3.019   c

3.020   c

3.021   b

3.022   a

3.023   d

3.024   d

3.025   d

3.026   frontal lobe

3.027   longitudinal fissure

3.028   neuron

3.029   tropism

3.030   balance

3.031

Organism	Type of organism
a. algae	b. producers
c. protozoa	d. primary consumers
e. fish	f. secondary consumer
g. bear	h. tertiary consumer
i. bacteria	j. decomposers

3.032   The farther away a biome is from the equator, or the greater the latitude, the colder the climate. The higher the elevation of the land (the altitude) the colder the temperature. Examples of biomes would be as follows (any 4): tundra, northern coniferous forests, temperate coniferous forests, deciduous forests, grasslands, savannas, deserts, chaparral, tropical rain forests, tropical seasonal forests.

3.033   Any order:

a. geotropism

b. phototropism

c. hydrotropism

3.034   Answers will vary depending upon tropism chosen. Answer should include the following: Auxins are produced which control plant cell growth. These auxins concentrate on one side of the plant and cause the plant to grow toward or away from the stimulus.

SELF TEST 1

1.01 a. anther with pollen
　　　b. filament
　　　c. stigma
　　　d. style
　　　e. ovary
　　　f. ovule
　　　g. petal
　　　h. receptacle
　　　i. sepal
　　　j. pistil

1.02 i

1.03 d

1.04 f

1.05 e

1.06 g

1.07 h

1.08 c

1.09 j

1.010 b

1.011 a

1.012 The stigma is sugary and permits the pollen to stick. The sugar stimulates the growth of pollen tubes. The tube grows down to the ovary and delivers the sperm cell.

1.013 Chromosome numbers are reduced to half the number so that when fertilization occurs, the original number is restored.

1.014 half the original number

1.015 If the anther with the pollen is below the stigma, the flower is generally cross-pollinated.

1.016 seven

1.017 ten

1.018 fourteen

1.019 female

1.020 undeveloped

1.021 pollen

1.022 sugar

1.023 self-pollinated

1.024 original

1.025 reproductive

1.026 true

1.027 false

1.028 false

1.029 true

1.030 true

1.031 false

1.032 true

1.033 false

1.034 true

1.035 true

SELF TEST 2

2.01　j

2.02　d

2.03　f

2.04　i

2.05　g

2.06　h

2.07　b

2.08　e

2.09　a

2.010　c

2.011　k

2.012　m

2.013　tall

2.014　dwarf

2.015　smooth

2.016　100%

2.017　nontasters

2.018　100%

2.019　seven

2.020　Example: He probably would never have been famous since he would not have discovered the principle of dominance.

2.021　The offspring resulting from a cross between two organisms differing in one or more genes. (Tt)

2.022　An organism having the same genes for a particular trait. (TT) or (tt)

2.023

	S	s
S	SS	Ss
s	Ss	ss

2.024　3/4　(SS, Ss, Ss)

2.025　1/4　(ss)

2.026　1/4　(SS)

2.027　1/4　(ss)

2.028　false

2.029　true

2.030　true

2.031　false

2.032　true

2.033　true

2.034　true

2.035　true

2.036　a

2.037　b

2.038　b

2.039　d

2.040　c

2.041　b

2.042　a

2.043　a

2.044　c

2.045　c

SELF TEST 3

3.01 h

3.02 k

3.03 b

3.04 c

3.05 n

3.06 g

3.07 m

3.08 j

3.09 i

3.010 e

3.011 d

3.012 a

3.013 f

3.014 false

3.015 true

3.016 false

3.017 false

3.018 true

3.019 false

3.020 true

3.021 true

3.022 true

3.023 false

3.024 Example: Seedless bananas, grapes, and oranges are mutations. These mutations are harmful to the plants but helpful in providing food.

3.025 Example: A person may have genes for tallness, but still be very short if nutrition is not adequate. Temperature changes the action of the genes for color in Siamese cats and Himalayan rabbits.

3.026 DNA is a double spiral like a staircase. The sides of the staircase are sugar (ribose) phosphate. The bases act like the cell's alphabet to spell traits.

3.027 DNA is very stable. Mutations rarely occur. Mutations are usually harmful and nearly always cause the loss of a trait. Mutations do not change the kinds.

3.028 Reproduction is by budding or grafting on to seeded types.

3.029 The offspring resulting from a cross between two organisms differing in one or more genes. Tt, Cc

3.030 An organism having the same genes for a particular trait. Tt, Cc

3.031 egg

3.032 multiple

3.033 mitosis

3.034 incomplete dominance

3.035 heredity

3.036 recessive

3.037 tall

3.038 nontasters

3.039

	C	c
C	CC	Cc
c	Cc	cc

SELF TEST 1

1.01   true

1.02   false

1.03   true

1.04   false

1.05   false

1.06   true

1.07   true

1.08   true

1.09   true

1.010   false

1.011   e

1.012   d

1.013   c

1.014   h

1.015   a

1.016   i

1.017   b

1.018   j

1.019   k

1.020   g

1.021   c. mass

1.022   c. the same as

1.023   a. has a fixed volume but takes the shape of its container

1.024   b. has the volume and shape of its container

1.025   c. has a fixed volume and shape

1.026   c. Robert Boyle

1.027   b. subatomic particles

1.028   b. 118

1.029   c. calcium carbonate

1.030   a. a million

1.031–1.032 Teacher/Adult check (Look for detail in drawings.)

1.033   a. no
        b. yes
        c. no
        d. no
        e. yes

1.034   It is a model of an atom that attempts to show that the electrons swarm around the nucleus in an incredibly fast way.

1.035   An element is a pure substance that cannot be broken down chemically into simpler substances.

SELF TEST 2

2.01	Cu		2.021	false
2.02	P		2.022	true
2.03	I		2.023	false
2.04	Ag		2.024	false
2.05	S		2.025	true
2.06	Mg		2.026	false
2.07	Fe		2.027	false
2.08	Au		2.028	true
2.09	U		2.029	true
2.010	Zn		2.030	false

2.011	c		2.031	chemical elements
2.012	f		2.032	1 (one)
2.013	h		2.033	protons
2.014	a		2.034	Hydrogen
2.015	i		2.035	2 (two)
2.016	e			
2.017	b		2.036	A plus-charged proton, a neutron with no charge (neutral), and an electron which is minus-charged.
2.018	g			
2.019	j		2.037	Man-made elements are made by increasing the proton number.
2.020	d			
			2.038	The mass would be the same. (Mass is the amount of matter).

SELF TEST 3

3.01	atomic structure	3.016	f
3.02	protons	3.017	i
3.03	atomic weight	3.018	b
3.04	Acids	3.019	h
3.05	neutralize	3.020	e

3.06 a. atomic number
      b. chemical symbol
      c. atomic weight

3.07 8 (eight)

3.08 8 (eight)

3.09 a. base
      b. acid
      c. base
      d. acid

3.010 Possible answers, any three: oranges, grapefruit, lemons, limes, vinegar, antiseptic salve, insecticides, paints, soaps

3.011 c

3.012 g

3.013 j

3.014 d

3.015 a

3.021 Li

3.022 K

3.023 Na

3.024 H

3.025 He

3.026 N

3.027 O

3.028 Ca

3.029 C

3.030 Cl

3.031 Teacher/Adult check. Answer must show 2 protons and 2 neutrons in the nucleus with 2 electrons in the first shell.

3.032 Answer may vary, but it should explain how elements, like chlorine, that do not have the full number of electrons in their outermost shells seek to fill them and join with elements that have only one, like sodium.

SELF TEST 1

1.01   b

1.02   c

1.03   i

1.04   k

1.05   j

1.06   l

1.07   h

1.08   g

1.09   d

1.010   f

1.011   true

1.012   true

1.013   true

1.014   true

1.015   true

1.016   true

1.017   true

1.018   true

1.019   true

1.020   true

1.021   a. waves

1.022   c. tightened vocal chords

1.023   c. waves

1.024   a. intensity

1.025   b. compressibility

1.026   c. the electromagnetic spectrum

1.027   a. wavelengths

1.028   c. transparent

1.029   b. only one part of

1.030   b. absorbed

1.031   a. compression

b. rarefaction

1.032   a. crest

b. wavelength

c. trough

1.033   Sound waves start vibrations on the sensitive part of your ear. As the sound waves reach the eardrum located within the ear, the eardrum begins to vibrate in the same way as the object that originally produced the sound. The vibrating eardrum, in turn, causes the bones of the middle ear to vibrate. These vibrations are transferred to the nerves in the inner ear. The nerves carry the messages to the brain, enabling us to interpret the sounds that we hear.

1.034   Light is strictly neither a wave nor a particle because in some experiments it behaves like a wave, but in other experiments it behaves more like a particle.

SELF TEST 2

2.01 g

2.02 f

2.03 a

2.04 h

2.05 c

2.06 i

2.07 b

2.08 k

2.09 e

2.010 d

2.011 false

2.012 true

2.013 false

2.014 true

2.015 true

2.016 b. violet

2.017 b. prism

2.018 c. white

2.019 c. red

2.020 c. bend

2.021 Sir Isaac Newton

2.022 Either order:
a. prism
b. drop of water

2.023 Either order:
a. spectrum
b. rainbow

2.024 light

2.025 red

2.026 spectrum

2.027 violet

2.028 rainbow

2.029 a. 1,100 feet per second
b. 186,000 miles per second

2.030 b. and c. either order
a. loudness
b. height (highness)
c. depth (lowness)

2.031 a. red
b. orange
c. yellow
d. green
e. blue
f. indigo
g. violet

2.032 Sound waves are vibrations that travel on air molecules. They consist of compressions and rarefactions.

2.033 Sound travels slower on a mountain top because fewer air molecules are present.

2.034 Teacher/Adult check. Answer should indicate that colors which have longer wavelengths are more likely to be seen in a sunset because they are seen longer each day.

SELF TEST 3

3.01	c. reflected	3.026	h
3.02	c. waves	3.027	e
3.03	c. black	3.028	b
3.04	d. violet	3.029	f
3.05	c. red	3.030	g
3.06	b. black	3.031	d
3.07	a. vibrations		
3.08	d. black	3.032	reflect light
3.09	c. 1,100 feet per second	3.033	a. reflected
			b. absorbed
3.010	false	3.034	yellow
3.011	false	3.035	orange
3.012	false	3.036	black
3.013	false	3.037	colors
3.014	true	3.038	white
3.015	false	3.039	black
3.016	true	3.040	colorants
3.017	true	3.041	absorb
3.018	false	3.042	reflect
3.019	true		

3.020 i

3.021 c

3.022 k

3.023 l

3.024 j

3.025 a

3.043 In order: Red, orange, yellow, green, blue, indigo, and violet.

3.044 The primary colors of light are red, green, and blue. When they are mixod, tho color whito is produced.

3.045 The primary colorants are red, yellow, and blue. When they are mixed, the color black is produced.

SELF TEST 1

1.01   g

1.02   e

1.03   d

1.04   j

1.05   a

1.06   h

1.07   k

1.08   b

1.09   c

1.010   i

1.011   true

1.012   false

1.013   true

1.014   false

1.015   true

1.016   true

1.017   false

1.018   true

1.019   true

1.020   true

1.021   100 foot-pounds

1.022   200 foot-pounds

1.023   370 foot-pounds

1.024   2,900 foot-pounds

1.025   2 newton-meters

1.026   60 kilogram-meters

1.027   gravity

1.028   motion

1.029   work

1.030   same

1.031   Answer may vary. Even when we do not appear to be moving, the earth is rotating around its axis and orbiting around the sun. Even the sun is in motion in the galaxy. The galaxy is in motion through the universe.

1.032   Since the rock was not moved any distance (200 pounds x 0 feet = 0 footpounds), no work was done.

1.033   Any order:
Muscular force–man pushing a piano
Wind force–windmill
Water force–water moving a turbine

SELF TEST 2

2.01   e

2.02   c

2.03   i

2.04   h

2.05   l

2.06   d

2.07   j

2.08   b

2.09   g

2.010   k

2.011   a

2.012   f

2.013   true

2.014   false

2.015   true

2.016   false

2.017   true

2.018   false

2.019   true

2.020   true

2.021   true

2.022   false

2.023   true

2.024   a. Inertia–the tendency of an object to remain at rest or continue in motion in a straight line with constant speed.

b. Second Law–The rate of change of movement of an object moving in a straight line is proportional to the size of the force applied to it and is in the same direction that the force is applied.

c. Third Law–For every action there is an equal and opposite reaction.

2.025   Zero or 0

2.026   10 x 2 = 20

2.027   6

2.028   James Watt

2.029   Examples, any order:
   a. gravity
   b. wind
   c. water

2.030   property that makes an object at rest remain at rest or one in motion to remain in motion unless acted upon by some outside force

2.031   gravity

2.032   inertia

2.033   700 foot-pounds

2.034   700 foot-pounds

2.035   700 foot-pounds

2.036   a. 8 x 127 = 1,016 foot-pounds
        b. 8 x 129 = 1,032 foot-pounds

2.037   Ron

2.038   2 HP (550 + 550 = 2 horsepower) or 1,100÷550 = 2

2.039   51 kilogram-meters

2.040   2,000 x 5,280 = 10,560,000 foot-pounds

2.041   muscular

2.042   Answer may vary. ...An object is pushed, pulled, lifted, moved, or carried through a distance from where a force was applied to it.

2.043   He computed that a horse could do 33,000 foot-pounds of work per minute. This number was divided by 60 because there are 60 seconds in a minute. As a result, he described a horsepower as being 550 foot-pounds of work being done per second.

SELF TEST 3

3.01   g

3.02   h

3.03   f

3.04   j

3.05   e

3.06   b

3.07   l

3.08   i

3.09   c

3.010   d

3.011   k

3.012   a

3.013   true

3.014   true

3.015   false

3.016   false

3.017   true

3.018   true

3.019   false

3.020   true

3.021   true

3.022   true

3.013   true

3.014   true

3.015   false

3.016   false

3.017   true

3.018   true

3.019   false

3.020   true

3.021   true

3.022   true

3.023   13 x 3 = 39

3.024   20 x 3 = 60

3.025   exerted

3.026   electricity

3.027   inertia

3.028   482 watt

3.029   152 x 10 = 1,520

3.030   20

3.031   gravity

3.032   the tendency of an object to remain at rest or to continue in motion in a straight line with constant speed unless acted upon by some outside force

3.033   a machine

3.034   2 HP

3.035   Answer may vary. The golf ball would keep traveling in a straight line at a constant speed until acted upon by another force.

3.036   Answer may vary. The golf ball could be trapped by the gravitational pull of another body and fall toward it, or it could strike another object in space.

3.037   Example: Machines require work to get started and work to be stopped. This motion decreases the amount of useful work obtained.

3.038   Example: Motion from falling water can be used to generate power.

3.039   Example: Muscular force is used to move. The force of gravity helps us maintain balance as we walk. The forces of wind and water are used as sources to generate electricity.

3.040   Example: All things are attracted to the center of the earth. Gravity keeps objects from falling into space.

SELF TEST 1

1.01   l

1.02   k

1.03   j

1.04   a

1.05   b

1.06   c

1.07   d

1.08   i

1.09   h

1.010   f

1.011   true

1.012   true

1.013   true

1.014   false

1.015   false

1.016   true

1.017   true

1.018   true

1.019   false

1.020   false

1.021   b. $23\frac{1}{2}°$

1.022   a. sunset

1.023   a. 15°

1.024   c. Greenwich, England

1.025   c. 5:00 A.M.

1.026   c. 366

1.027   c. winter

1.028   a. ellipse or oval

1.029   c. reversed

1.030   c. the winter

1.031   c. 101,000

1.032   Any order:

   a. rotates about its axis

   b. orbits around the sun

   c. moves with sun around the center of the Milky Way Galaxy

   d. moves with Milky Way Galaxy through the universe

1.033   Night and day occur as the earth rotates about it axis. The sun shines on one side of the earth as it rotates (daylight), and the other side of earth is hidden from the sun (night).

1.034   The four seasons are spring, fall, summer, and winter. The seasons occur because the earth is tilted on its axis at $23\frac{1}{2}°$ and the earth is orbiting around the sun. When the Northern Hemisphere is tilted more toward the sun, it is summer in the Northern Hemisphere. The temperatures are then warmer. In the winter, the Northern Hemisphere is tilted away from the sun. The temperatures are then colder.

1.035   At the vernal equinox, the sun is directly over the equator at noon, and the day and night are equal length. As the earth continues to orbit around the sun, the days get longer in the Northern Hemisphere. At the autumnal equinox, the sun is directly overhead the equator at noon and the days and nights are equal length. As the earth continues to orbit around the sun, the days in the Northern Hemisphere get shorter.

SELF TEST 2

2.01   d

2.02   h

2.03   e

2.04   a

2.05   g

2.06   c

2.07   f

2.08   b

2.09   false

2.010   true

2.011   false

2.012   false

2.013   false

2.014   true

2.015   true

2.016   false

2.017   Either answer:
  inertia
  gravity

2.018   93,000,000 miles

2.019   Any order:
  a. Eastern
  b. Central
  c. Mountain
  d. Pacific

2.020   23 1/2°

2.021   leap year

2.022   the earth, moon, and sun are nearly in a straight line and the moon passes between the earth and sun.

2.023   the earth, moon, and sun are nearly in a straight line and the moon passes through the earth's shadow.

2.024   orbit

2.025   a.

2.026   c.

2.027   c.

2.028   b.

2.029   c.

2.030   During a solar eclipse, the line-up is sun, moon, and earth. During a lunar eclipse, the line-up is sun, earth, and moon.

2.031   A solar eclipse is rare because the moon's orbit is tilted about five degrees away from the earth's orbit. The earth's shadow and the moon's shadow usually go into space without touching either body. The moon and the earth travel either above or below, not in, the shadow of the other.

SELF TEST 3

3.01   false

3.02   true

3.03   false

3.04   true

3.05   true

3.06   true

3.07   false

3.08   false

3.09   false

3.010   false

3.011   true

3.012   g

3.013   f

3.014   l

3.015   i

3.016   h

3.017   e

3.018   k

3.019   j

3.020   c

3.021   b

3.022   a. Mercury

b. Venus

c. Earth

d. Mars

e. Jupiter

f. Saturn

g. Uranus

h. Neptune

3.023   c. 99

3.024   b. nuclear fusion

3.025   a. 10,000

3.026   b. a magnetic field

3.027   b. 25 days 9 hours

3.028   b. prominences

3.029   a. Northern Lights

3.030   a. no

3.031   b. 200 or more years

3.032   c. 500

3.033   Comets are bright objects in space with a nucleus made up of frozen water, carbon dioxide, methane, and ammonia, with dust and rocky material buried in it. They have long, elliptical orbits around the sun. Gas and dust are given off as the comet nears the sun, the heat melting the ice. This gas and dust form a large sphere around the nucleus. As the gas and dust stream into space they form the tail of the comet.

3.034   A meteoroid consists of particles of dust and very small rocks in space. When they enter the earth's atmosphere, they are called meteors or "shooting stars." When these hit the earth, they are called meteorites.

SELF TEST 1

1.01 e

1.02 f

1.03 h

1.04 l

1.05 k

1.06 j

1.07 d

1.08 c

1.09 g

1.010 i

1.011 true

1.012 false

1.013 true

1.014 true

1.015 false

1.016 true

1.017 false

1.018 true

1.019 true

1.020 false

1.021 4

1.022 2

1.023 5

1.024 1

1.025 3

1.026 reflecting

1.027 radio waves from outer space

1.028 Hawaii

1.029 Egyptians

1.030 Pluto

1.031 Astronomy is the science of the study of the stars, planets, and other objects that make up the universe. Astrology is an occult practice that attempts to predict human affairs and events on the earth from the positions of the stars.

1.032 Answer may vary. Adult check.

1.033 Any two of the following:

– he invented the reflecting telescope

– he discovered the law of gravitation

– he discovered that visible light can be broken down into a spectrum

1.034 Einstein revolutionized our concepts about mass, energy, space, and time through his theories of relativity. His work helps astronomers understand certain aspects of the universe, such as the way stars get their energy and produce light through the transformation of mass into energy.

SELF TEST 2

2.01   j

2.02   i

2.03   h

2.04   l

2.05   f

2.06   e

2.07   d

2.08   c

2.09   a

2.010   k

2.011   true

2.012   false

2.013   false

2.014   true

2.015   true

2.016   true

2.017   false

2.018   true

2.019   true

2.020   false

2.021   the stars, planets, and other objects in the universe

2.022   Pluto

2.023   core

2.024   radio waves from outer space

2.025   Egyptians

2.026   Either order:
   a. color
   b. temperature, size, or distance

2.027   reflecting

2.028   Fraunhofer

2.029   close

2.030   gas

2.031   The color of a star indicates its surface temperature. The hotter the star, the greater its brightness and the difference of its color.

2.032   Fraunhofer lines are lines found in the dark-line spectrum. Atoms of each chemical element produce a certain set of spectral lines (Fraunhofer lines). This knowledge enabled astronomers to identify elements that make up a star by studying the spectral lines in a star's light.

2.033   Answer may vary. Adult check.

2.034   Answer may vary. Example: With our normal eyesight, unaided by a telescope, a star may appear to be bright in comparison to other stars. However, a very bright star may appear dimmer than a less luminous star just because it is farther away from our solar system.

SELF TEST 3

3.01	Ursa Major	3.023	true
3.02	asterism	3.024	true
3.03	the Big Dipper	3.025	true
3.04	any order: a. Greeks b. Romans	3.026	b Ursa Minor
		3.027	c Amos 5:8
3.05	sextant	3.028	a the North Star
		3.029	c Orion
3.06	c	3.030	b Taurus
3.07	i	3.031	c Orion
3.08	f	3.032	b Roman gods
3.09	l	3.033	b Bootes
3.010	k	3.034	c absolute magnitude
3.011	g	3.035	a astronomy
3.012	j		
3.013	d	3.036	He telleth the number of the stars; he calleth them all by their names.
3.014	a		
3.015	m	3.037	An astrolabe was used to measure the stars' angles as they appeared above the northern horizon. This was useful for navigators and sailors to determine their location.
3.016	e		
3.017	h		
3.018	b		
3.019	true	3.038	Constellations are groups of stars within a particular region of the sky. In this sense, they are real. However, the patterns that were made up by sailors, farmers, and astronomers in ancient days were imaginary. In that sense, they are not real.
3.020	false		
3.021	false		
3.022	true		

SELF TEST 1

1.01	l
1.02	m
1.03	k
1.04	i
1.05	j
1.06	h
1.07	g
1.08	n
1.09	p
1.010	f
1.011	e
1.012	d
1.013	a
1.014	b
1.015	c

1.016	true
1.017	false
1.018	true
1.019	true
1.020	false
1.021	true
1.022	true
1.023	false
1.024	true
1.025	false
1.026	false

1.027	true
1.028	true
1.029	true
1.030	false

1.031	knee
1.032	sun
1.033	phloem
1.034	light
1.035	water
1.036	bile
1.037	away from
1.038	blood
1.039	clavicle
1.040	leg
1.041	skull (head)
1.042	neuron
1.043	synapse
1.044	Mendel
1.045	DNA

1.046   Voluntary muscles are controlled by command. Involuntary muscles operate without thinking.

1.047   Example:

Animals consume the oxygen given off by plants and release carbon dioxide and water which plants consume.

SELF TEST 2

2.01   e

2.02   h

2.03   c

2.04   b

2.05   k

2.06   d

2.07   i

2.08   a

2.09   g

2.010   f

2.011   a.   K

      b.   He

      c.   H

      d.   F

      e.   Na

      f.   S

      g.   Cl

      h.   Ca

2.012   a. calcium

      b. nitrogen

      c. magnesium

      d. cobalt

      e. uranium

      f. copper

      g. potassium

      h. phosphorus

      i. lead

      j. oxygen

      k. silicon

      l. nickel

2.013   true

2.014   true

2.015   false

2.016   true

2.017   false

2.018   true

2.019   true

2.020   true

2.021   true

2.022   true

2.023   true

2.024   false

2.025   true

2.026   true

2.027   Example:

The electromagnetic spectrum consists of the visible and invisible parts of the spectrum. The visible part is only a small portion of the electromagnetic spectrum.

2.028   Example:

Sound waves travel on air molecules. They travel by a series of compressions and rarefactions.

SELF TEST 3

3.01	l
3.02	h
3.03	j
3.04	p
3.05	e
3.06	d
3.07	f
3.08	q
3.09	s
3.010	n
3.011	i
3.012	o
3.013	b
3.014	a
3.015	g
3.016	t
3.017	k
3.018	m

3.019	true
3.020	false
3.021	false
3.022	false
3.023	true
3.024	true
3.025	truc
3.026	false
3.027	true
3.028	true
3.029	false
3.030	true

3.031 Any order:

a. color

b. size

c. distance, or temperature, brightness

3.032 elements or materials

3.033 atom

3.034 it is closer to us than others

3.035 10,000°F

3.036 evaporation of perspiration

3.037 fats

3.038 leaf

3.039 a major ecological grouping of plants and animals

3.040 a. K

b. Fe

c. Na

d. Ni

e. C

3.041 During a solar eclipse, the sun is darkened because the moon passes between the earth and the sun for a short time. A lunar eclipse: the earth casts a shadow on the moon.

3.042 It is important because it helps to identify elements as in the discovery of helium. Helium is a very useful substance.

3.043 The air sacs of the lungs pick up oxygen on hemoglobin. It is carried on the hemoglobin to various body cells.

3.044 A natural plant regulator is one that is made in the plant. An artificial one is a chemical put on a plant by people.

1. a
2. g
3. f
4. j
5. c
6. i
7. e
8. h
9. d
10. b

11. cuticle
12. epidermis
13. chloroplast
14. xylem
15. phloem

16. d. epidermis
17. b. root hair
18. a. vascular cylinder
19. e. root cap
20. c. cortex

21. a
22. b
23. a
24. d
25. c
26. d
27. d
28. a
29. a
30. c

31. Any order:
   a. color of light
   b. amount of water and/or minerals
   c. amount of carbon dioxide

32. Answers may vary. Any order:
   a. can cause cancer in man and animals
   b. may kill plants you don't want killed

1. c

2. e

3. b

4. d

5. a

6. f

7. e

8. b

9. a

10. c

11. false

12. true

13. true

14. false

15. true

16. Either order:
   a. grinding or chewing
   b. breaking down food for body use

17. Any order:
   a. exercise
   b. cleanliness
   c. good diet

18. Any order:
   a. kidneys and skin
   b. lungs
   c. circulation (blood) system

19. atrium

20. heart murmur

21.–25.   Examples:

21. a. cranium or skull
    b. head

22. a. clavicle or collar bone
    b. chest

23. a. ilium
    b. hip

24. a. femur
    b. leg

25. a. patella or knee cap
    b. leg

26. a. striated
    b. skeletal muscles (legs, arms, trunk)

27. a. smooth
    b. internal muscles (intestines, stomach, blood vessels)

28. a. cardiac
    b. heart

29.–31.   Any order; Examples:

29. cancer

30. heart disease

31. tuberculosis

32. h

33. d, e

34. b, c, f, g

35. e

36. a, g

1. false
2. true
3. true
4. false
5. true
6. true
7. true
8. false
9. true
10. true
11. a. cerebrum
    b. cerebellum
    c. brain stem
    d. frontal lobe
    e. temporal lobe
    f. parietal lobe
    g. occipital lobe
    h. left cerebral hemisphere
    i. right cerebral hemisphere
    j. longitudinal fissure

12. a
13. c
14. e
15. g
16. f
17. a
18. b
19. a
20. a
21. d
22. j
23. i
24. h

25. i
26. h
27. f
28. h
29. g
30. i
31. k
32. j
33. d
34. l
35. b
36. e
37. c. terrestrial biomes
38. a. producers
39. b. parasitism
40. d. phototropism
41. c. cell body
42. Teacher/Adult check
43. Tropisms are caused by the accumulation of auxins in a certain part of a plant. Auxins can speed up or slow down cell growth in a plant.
44. Any 5, any order:
    tundra
    northern coniferous forests
    deciduous forests
    grasslands
    tropical rain forests
    deserts

1. c

2. e

3. s

4. d

5. f

6. t

7. u

8. r

9. q

10. p

11. o

12. n

13. l

14. m

15. k

16. b

17. i

18. h

19. g

20. j

21. a

22. false

23. true

24. false

25. false

26. true

27. false

28. true

29. true

30. false

31. false

32. true

33. c

34. b

35. b

36. c

37. b

38. c

39. A change in a gene–a mistake or a misprint.

40. Example: Rather than showing dominance, there is a blending of traits, for example, getting pink flowers instead of all red when blending white and red four o'clocks..

41. Examples: seedless bananas, seedless grapes, seedless oranges, thornless berries, pumpkins with seeds that have no hulls

42. When the white hair on the Himalayan rabbit and the Siamese cat was shaved off and cold applied to the area, black hair grew back in its place.

43. Chromosome numbers are reduced to half the number so that when fertilization occurs, the original number is restored.

44. Any 5, any order:

   a. anther

   b. filament

   c. stigma

   d. style

   e. ovary

   or: ovule, petal, sepal, receptacle, pistil, or stamen

45. a. DNA is a double spiral like a staircase or ladder

   b. the sides are sugar (ribose) phosphate

   c. bases act like the cell's alphabet to spell traits

1. e
2. g
3. a
4. f
5. b
6. q
7. c
8. k
9. n
10. l
11. m
12. o
13. i
14. j
15. h

16. true
17. false
18. true
19. true
20. true
21. true
22. true
23. false
24. true
25. false

26. c. mass
27. c. the same as
28. a. has a fixed volume but takes the shape of its container
29. a. a million
30. a. protons
31. b. hydrogen
32. a. two
33. b. atomic weight
34. c. acids
35. b. neutralize

36. Li
37. Na
38. He
39. Ca
40. Cl

41. Teacher/Adult check. Answer must show 2 protons and 2 neutrons in the nucleus with 2 electrons in the first shell.

42. It is a model of an atom that attempts to show that the electrons swarm around the nucleus in an incredibly fast way.

1. f
2. g
3. h
4. a
5. i
6. k
7. j
8. b
9. l
10. d

11. true
12. true
13. true
14. true
15. true
16. false
17. false
18. true
19. false
20. true

21. a. waves
22. b. compressibility
23. c. the electromagnetic spectrum
24. a. wavelengths
25. c. transparent
26. b. absorbed
27. b. violet
28. c. red
29. b. reflected
30. b. black

31. red
32. Any of the following: radio waves, microwaves, infrared, ultraviolet, x-rays, gamma rays, or cosmic rays
33. violet
34. yellow
35. orange
36. white
37. colorants
38. Noises
39. faster
40. wavelengths

41. Sound waves start vibrations on the sensitive part of your ear. As the sound waves reach the eardrum located within the ear, the eardrum begins to vibrate in the same way as the object that originally produced the sound. The vibrating eardrum, in turn, causes the bones of the middle ear to vibrate. These vibrations are transferred to the nerves in the inner ear. The nerves carry the messages to the brain, enabling us to interpret the sounds that we hear.

42. The primary colors of light are red, green, and blue. When they are mixed, the color white is produced.

1. e
2. c
3. h
4. d
5. a
6. b
7. g
8. i
9. j
10. f

11. true
12. true
13. true
14. false
15. true
16. false
17. false
18. true
19. true
20. true

21. b
22. d or a
23. a or d

24. b
25. a or b
26. b
27. c
28. d
29. a
30. c

31. electricity or power
32. Work in equals work out
33. James Watt
34. mechanical device
35. inertia
36. distance
37. muscular
38. no
39. 20 x 2 = 40 kilogram-meters
40. 40 newton-meters

41. Example: As you travel along in a car, you are in motion compared to a sign on the highway, but you are stationary compared to the person sitting next to you.

42. Example: Straight motion can be changed by a windmill or a water wheel to produce electricity.

1. j
2. k
3. a
4. b
5. m
6. l
7. c
8. i
9. d
10. h
11. e

12. false
13. false
14. true
15. true
16 true
17. true
18. true
19. false
20. true
21. false
22. false

23. a. Mercury
     b. Venus
     c. Earth
     d. Mars
     e. Jupiter
     f. Saturn
     g. Uranus
     h. Neptune

24. Any order:
    a. rotates about its axis
    b. orbits around the sun
    c. moves with sun around the center of the Milky Way Galaxy
    d. moves with Milky Way Galaxy through the universe

25. b. 23 $\frac{1}{2}$°

26. a. sunset

27. c. 101,000

28. a. the earth

29. c. solar eclipse

30. c. 99

31. a. helium

32. b. 25 days 9 hours

33. From the rising of the sun unto the going down of the same the Lord's name is to be praised.

34. Night and day occur as the earth rotates about its axis. The sun shines on one side of the earth as it rotates (daylight), and the other side of earth is hidden from the sun (night).

35. The four seasons are spring, fall, summer, and winter. The seasons occur because the earth is tilted on its axis at 23 $\frac{1}{2}$° and the earth is orbiting around the sun. When the Northern Hemisphere is tilted more toward the sun, it is summer in the Northern Hemisphere. The temperatures are then warmer. In the winter, the Northern Hemisphere is tilted away from the sun. The temperatures are then colder.

1. e
2. f
3. g
4. a
5. h
6. i
7. k
8. b
9. c
10. d

11. true
12. false
13. false
14. true
15. true
16. true
17. true
18. false
19. true
20. true

21. c. reflecting
22. a. radio waves from space
23. b. Hawaii
24. c. the dwarf planet Pluto
25. a. core
26. b. Fraunhofer

27. b. Ursa Minor
28. c. winter
29. c. Orion
30. c. Orion

31. 4
32. 1
33. 5
34. 2
35. 3

36. Astronomy is the science of the study of the stars, planets, and other objects that make up the universe. Astrology is an occult practice that attempts to predict human affairs and events on the earth from the positions of the stars.

37. Yes, Christians can accept astronomy as a science. Astronomy can help Christians explain much about the physical universe that God has created. However, for Christians, any explanation of the universe and its workings must be compatible with our belief that God created the universe and that He is in control of it.

38. The color of a star indicates its surface temperature. The hotter the star, the greater its brightness.

39. Example: In 1993, the shuttle astronauts were sent to the Hubble Space Telescope because it had a faulty mirror that had to be replaced. The shuttle astronauts changed the mirror and the telescope can see clearer than ever.

Science 610 Test Key

1. s
2. k
3. i
4. l
5. f
6. g
7. j
8. b
9. h
10. m
11. a
12. n
13. o
14. q
15. p
16. e
17. d
18. c

19. true
20. true
21. false
22. false
23. true
24. true
25. true
26. false
27. false
28. true
29. true

30.
a. potassium
b. sodium
c. nitrogen
d. oxygen
e. carbon
f. hydrogen

31. Any order:
a. color
b. spectrum
c. size or temperature, brightness

32. elements on the sun (stars)
33. it is close to us
34. muscular coordination
35. intelligence and thought
36. red blood cells and white cells
37. synapse
38. a layer of brilliant red gases above the photosphere of the sun
39. June 21

40. During a solar eclipse, the sun is darkened because the moon passes between the earth and the sun. During a lunar eclipse, the moon is darkened because earth casts a shadow on the moon.

41. The skin is a protective coat that prevents dirt and germs from entering the body. It also cools the body by evaporation of perspiration. It serves to keep contact with the environment by nerve endings.

42. The major characteristic is its dryness. Few animals, mostly rodents and snakes, can survive the dryness. Large cacti with thick leaves are about the only plants that can survive.

43. A new era in space exploration began with the launch of the Russian satellite Sputnik in 1957. Unmanned space observatories and probes have been sent to other bodies in our solar system since then. In 1990, the Hubble Space telescope was launched, revealing much more detail about our universe than earth-based telescopes. In 1999, the Chandra X-ray Observatory was launched and promises to give even more detail. There have also been a number of new earth-based telescopes built since the 1950s.

1. c
2. e
3. h
4. b
5. j
6. i
7. a
8. f
9. g
10. d
11. b
12. e
13. a
14. c
15. d
16. vascular cylinder
17. root hair
18. cortex
19. epidermis
20. root cap
21. b

22. a
23. c
24. c
25. c
26. a
27. c
28. b
29. c
30. d
31. Answers may vary. Examples; any order:

    a. Auxin causes young cells to grow longer than normal.

    b. Gibberellin helps corn and wheat grow three to five times as tall as normal.

    c. Auxin can produce tomatoes with no seeds.

32. Answers may vary. Examples; either order:

    a. Some artificial regulators are selective. They kill weeds but not crops.

    b. Yields are greater so prices are lower.

1. mouth
2. esophagus
3. stomach
4. pancreas
5. small intestine
6. rectum

7. c
8. b
9. a
10. d

11. true
12. false
13. true
14. false
15. false

16. a. cut
    b. grind
17. Examples; either order:
    a. liver
    b. pancreas or gall bladder
18. Examples; either order:
    a. cleanliness
    b. proper diet or plenty of fluid
19. ventricle
20. valves

21. Answers may vary. Examples:
    a. femur
    b. spinal column
    c. skull
22. cardiac
23. smooth
24. striated
25. a. a, e, f, or h
    b. a, e, f, or h
26. Either order:
    a. b
    b. i
27. j
28. d
29. Either order:
    a. g
    b. e
30. a
31. Answers may vary. Examples; either order:
    a. Air pollution robs cells of oxygen and poisons cells.
    b. Smoking is a prime cause of lung cancer and other lung diseases. Or:
    c. Coal dust with poor air circulation in coal mines causes "black lung".
32. Answers may vary. Any order:
    a. muscular dystrophy
    b. rickets
    c. cancer of the bones

1. j

2. f

3. b

4. h

5. l

6. i

7. d

8. k

9. o

10. m

11. n

12. g

13. e

14. a

15. c

16. a. geotropism

17. b. phototropism

18. c. spinal cord

19. d. plexus

20. b. tropical forest

21. desert

22. auxin

23. a cluster of neurons

24. man

25. produce high-level thought

26. process that starts at one point, goes through a series of steps, and ends up back at the beginning

27. Example: ocean or fresh water pond

28. automatic response

29. instinct

30. learning that takes place by trying many things one at a time until the right choice is found

31. c

32. c

33. b

34. c

35. a

36. a. seed

   b. bird

   c. weasel

   d. lion

   e. bacteria

   f. producer

   g. consumer

   h. consumer

   i. consumer

   j. decomposer

1. Example:

   They are budded or grafted to a seeded stump.

2. Example:

   DNA is very stable. Mutations provide only variety within the kinds. Mutations do not build up; they tear down. They are very rare and usually harmful.

3. spiral-shaped or contains deoxyribose or has four bases as an alphabet

4. Examples:

   Mutations for thornless berries, seedless grapes, and seedless oranges are helpful to man.

5. Examples:

   A person may have genes for tallness but will not be tall if he does not get adequate food. Genes of the Siamese cat or Himalayan rabbit react with cool temperatures.

6. d
7. f
8. h
9. c
10. j
11. g
12. i
13. e
14. b
15. k

16. true
17. true
18. true
19. true
20. true
21. true
22. false
23. false
24. true
25. true

26. c. incomplete dominance
27. a. a trait
28. b. cross-pollination
29. c. hybrid
30. b. new cells with half the number of chromosomes

31. Examples:

    a. stigma

    b. style

    c. anther (or pollen, filament, or ovary)

32. Examples:

    a. The DNA molecule with its bases is able to spell out different traits.

    b. The environmental influence on traits also provides variety.

OR: Dominance and recessiveness also provide some variety. Mutations provide some variety.

1. d
2. a
3. e
4. j
5. g
6. h
7. i
8. f
9. c
10. b
11. true
12. true
13. false
14. false
15. true
16. true
17. true
18. true
19. true
20. false
21. H
22. Ca
23. Cl
24. Mg
25. Zn
26. Ag
27. I
28. S
29. Si

30. P
31. Fe
32. He
33. c. gas
34. c. fixed shape
35. b. an element
36. b. the shape of the container
37. c. gas
38. a. number of protons
39. c. protons plus neutrons
40. c. acetic acid
41. Example: An electron cloud model is used to show what an atom may look like at any time.
42. a. 7 = atomic number (number of protons)

b. N = nitrogen symbol

c. 14 = atomic weight (protons + neutrons)

43. Example: Chlorine has 7 electrons in its M shell and needs 8 electrons to become stable. Sodium has only one electron in its M shell and will "fit the bill."

44. Any order:
a. protons
b. neutrons
c. electrons
45. hydrogen
46. carbon

Science 606 Alternate Test Key

1. true
2. true
3. true
4. true
5. true
6. true
7. false
8. false
9. 186,000
10. 1,100
11. crest
12. trough
13. air
14. slower
15. opaque, or name a specific material such as lead or brick
16. electromagnetic spectrum
17. red
18. violet
19. Examples:

X-rays, cosmic rays, radio waves, ultraviolet, microwave, electricity, radar
20. all of the radiation received by planet earth
21. Newton
22. darkness
23. spectrum
24. Any order:
 a. red
 b. yellow
 c. blue
25. Any order:
 a. red
 b. green
 c. blue
26. black
27. soak up or take up
28. green
29. e
30. b
31. j
32. i
33. h
34. f
35. k
36. g
37. d
38. c

1. j
2. e
3. a
4. f
5. c
6. d
7. g
8. b
9. h
10. i

11. true
12. false
13. false
14. false
15. false
16. true
17. false
18. true
19. false
20. false
21. true
22. true
23. true
24. true
25. true

26. b
27. d

28. a
29. a
30. b
31. d
32. c
33. c
34. b
35. d

36. power
37. electricity
38. force
39. kilogram-meter
40. distance
41. inertia
42. motion
43. work
44. push or pull
45. gravity

46. Look for the general idea. Example: the tendency of an object to remain at rest or continue motion in a straight line with constant speed

47. Look for the general idea. Example: All matter is attracted to other matter in the universe.

48. Look for the general idea. Example: by the use of turbines

1. d
2. e
3. i
4. j
5. f
6. k
7. g
8. h
9. l
10. b
11. c

12. true
13. false
14. true
15. true
16. true
17 true

18. equinox
19. meteorite
20. 7,900
21. Either order:
    a. oxygen (or air)
    b. water
22. eight

23. partial
24. 23 1/2°
25. solar
26. Example: its rotation about its axis from west to east (or counterclockwise motion as seen from above the north pole).
27. equal
28. Sir Isaac Newton
29. orbit around the sun
30. comets
31. meteoroid
32. 10,000°F
33. The moon crosses the path between the earth and the sun, casting a dark shadow on the earth called the umbra.
34. Any three of these, and any order:
    a. rotates about its axis
    b. orbits around the sun
    c. moves with sun around the center of the Milky Way Galaxy
    d. moves with Milky Way Galaxy through the universe
35. The sun is directly overhead at noon at the equator. The days and nights are equal length.
36. a. Mercury
    b. Venus
    c. Earth

1. d
2. e
3. f
4. g
5. a
6. h
7. i
8. k
9. j
10. l
11. m
12. n
13. o
14. c
15. b
16. true
17. true
18. true
19. true
20. false
21. true
22. true
23. true
24. false
25. false
26. true

27. Orion
28. Any of the following:
    size
    color
    temperature
    brightness
    distance
29. 6
30. Minor
31. 92,900,000 miles
32. a piece of plastic with grooves that make a spectrum like a prism
33. Orion
34. relativity
35. Bootes
36. Mars
37. hydrogen
38. Hyades or Pleiades
39. charged particles which enter the earth's magnetic fields
40. Example: by the star Polaris
41. Example:
    It was discovered by a dark line in the spectrum. It was identified on the sun before it was identified on earth.
42. Example:
    The Lord can count and name the stars.
43. Example:
    He created all things for His pleasure.

1. d
2. i
3. e
4. a
5. k
6. c
7. o
8. j
9. b
10. p
11. n
12. r
13. m
14. l
15. f
16. h
17. s
18. q

19. true
20. false
21. false
22. true
23. true
24. false
25. true
26. false
27. true
28. false
29. true

30.
   a. helium
   b. sodium
   c. chlorine
   d. sulfur
   e. calcium
   f. iron

31. Any order:
   a. solid
   b. liquid
   c. gas

32. weight
33. Date Line
34. oval
35. eclipse
36. planet
37. helium

38. Example:
   A voluntary muscle can be controlled at will; an involuntary muscle is automatic.

39. Example:
   The lungs pick up oxygen and get rid of carbon dioxide waste.

40. Example:
   A tropical rain forest biome has a hot and humid climate; plant life is abundant; and many species of animals can be supported.

41. Example:
   The cerebellum coordinates muscle movements.